HARD-BOILED is a one-of-a-k  game.

HARD-BOILED is like reading a Raymond Chandler novel or watching *The Maltese Falcon*, only this time *you* are the world-weary dick cracking wise to every dame and copper.

HARD-BOILED gives you the absorbing involvement and character interaction of a role-playing game, without the need of an expensive computer or a third party "master" or referee.

Instead, for each case, you distribute a certain number of Muscle, Moxie, and Magnetism points (M–M–M points) that makes up your personality as a private detective. These points are used in your investigation in order to obtain clues for the case. Some lug may sap you (Muscle points), or some fast talk may get you out of a jam (Moxie points), or maybe just an easy line to a hard dame may spill some revealing beans (Magnetism points).

HARD-BOILED gives you the logical deductive puzzles of a mystery game, without the simple-minded repetitiveness of always deducing, "Colonel Whosits with the Whatsits in the Wherever."

Instead, for each case, you are presented with a different cast of characters, different locations, and different crimes. Best of all, and *as in no other game*, you find out what your winning objectives are as the game progresses. That is, you may be told at the start that two of your five objectives are to find out Who killed Moose McPhee? and Why? But you will have to discover the other three objectives during the course of the game. You may run into yet another dead body and so have to find yet another murderer and motive, or you may stumble onto a blackmail plot and have to find out who is behind it. And so is woven the web of good hard-boiled thrillers. No other game book recreates a detective mystery in this way.

HARD-BOILED can be played solitaire or in collaboration with a friend or two. You don't need a board, cards, markers, or money. All you need is your smarts and a pair of dice (trench and fedora optional).

HARD-BOILED

•••••• **HARD-BOILED**

Three Tough Cases
for the Private Eye with Smarts

by
Robert DiChiara

illustrated by
Joe Servello

DAVID R. GODINE, PUBLISHER • Boston

First published in 1985 by
David R. Godine, Publisher, Inc.
306 Dartmouth Street
Boston, Massachusetts 02116

Library of Congress Cataloging in Publication Data

DiChiara, Robert.
  Hard-boiled : three tough cases for the private eye with smarts.

  1. Games.   2. Dice.   3. Detective and mystery stories.   I. Title.
GV1312.D52   1985   795.1   84-48324
ISBN 0-87923-554-3

First printing
Printed in the United States of America

To my Mom,
To my Dad,
To my shweetheart and best Gal Friday—Elaine

And a doff of the fedora to all the Joes and Mabels who leveled with me and made sure I didn't gum up the works—in other words, to the good people who play-tested various cases for this book or encouraged me even when it was but a gun barrel's gleam in this author's peepers: Deborah Rubin, Ed Yankov, Dennis Vellucci, Llynne Catarsi, Mike Anzelone, Robert Hommel, Carl Patrick, Irene Brenalvirez, Fred Linck & Donna McAleer, Robert & Cindy Nash, Jay Silverman, John Tucker, Walter Stepp, Fran O'Connor, Allen Kupfer, Sarah Saint-Onge . . . and especially Walter Raubicheck, forever Spade to my Marlowe.

Contents

How to Play

Get a pencil, some paper, and a pair of six-sided dice. Turn to the Case Opening of your choice and read it. The Opening will set the scene and give you:

- a client (usually)
- two or three objectives to solve (more appear later in the game)
- the case's difficulty, rated in bullets (0–5, 5 being the toughest)
- locations on a map of Los Angeles that you must mark with a star (you visit these locations to solve the case)
- the total number of Muscle, Moxie, and Magnetism points (M–M–M points) that make up your private eye personality for that case.

Objectives

Be sure to write down each objective as you learn it. Don't abbreviate—you need to be absolutely certain of what you're looking for. You'll want to refer to your objectives throughout the game, making notes whenever a new clue pops up, another suspect surfaces, or you just get a good idea. Hey, you may be a crack detective, but you're not Mr. Memory.

Map of Los Angeles

Each case has its own special map of Los Angeles, highlighting certain locations that you will visit during the game. Each location has a paragraph number assigned to it. The only things you must remember are: a) never visit a location that has no star or only a crossed-out star beside it; b) whenever you are told to cross out a star, do just that—DO NOT

ERASE—because a crossed-out star means you've already visited a location and also affects your next move. Also, make sure you cross out ONLY ONE star, as some locations might collect a few, meaning you will be making more than one visit during the game.

M–M–M Points

At the top of your note paper, make three columns labeled Muscle, Moxie, and Magnetism. Before you start to play, distribute the M–M–M point total found in the Case Opening any way you like among the three columns, according to how important a role you think each characteristic is going to play in the game (for example, you might choose to give yourself more Muscle, expecting to meet more thugs than femmes fatales).

During a case, you will have to make decisions on how to use your M–M–M points. Do you climb through a mobster's window or put a tail on his best gal? Should you slug a chump or just slip him a smooth line? Most times, your choices will use up valuable M–M–M points. Sometimes they mean life or death . . . yours. Go with your best hunch. When you are directed to subtract or add a certain number of points from/to a particular M–M–M column, you'll see a formula similar to this: "Subtract D + 2 Muscle points" (for example)—this means that you should throw the dice, add two to the roll, and then subtract the total from the Muscle column.

You should not stop subtracting points from an M–M–M column just because you hit zero—continue into negative numbers. During the game, you face death *only* when you go into negative numbers. (A gun symbol ☞ next to a paragraph will signal such fatal danger.) And, at the end of the game, the negative numbers will be subtracted from your score.

AFTER READING THE CASE OPENING, writing
down your objectives, figuring out your M–M–M points,
and starring your map, you begin playing by hitting the
street and reading paragraph #1. From then on, all you have
to do is follow *all* instructions as they appear in the game.

THE GAME IS OVER when you are at paragraph #1 and
all stars on the map are crossed out—i.e., you have no place
else to go. This means you have all the clues needed to solve
the case. Take a moment to reread the case opening, just to
refresh your memory and see if you missed anything. Then
write out a solution for each objective on a clean sheet of paper. Answer completely and specifically—don't, for example, just write "jealousy" as a motive; say who was jealous of
whom and why. Some cases, especially those involving
murder, might have someone behind a crime who did not
actually commit it, but who is nevertheless responsible (for
example, a boss who tells one of his thugs to rub somebody
out is the real culprit—the thug is only an instrument). It is
important to be as thorough as possible, because each por-
tion of the solution carries a certain number of points—the
more questions you get right, the more facts you list, the
higher your score.

When you have finished writing out your deductions,
turn to the solution page and "The Final Dope" for your
case. The solution sheet will list the correct answers to all
the objectives and tell you how many points each answer is
worth. After you've totalled your points, subtract all your
negative M–M–M points—the result will be your score.
Then check to see how well you did by looking at the
HARD-BOILED rating system for the case.

After this, just so you know the whole story, read
"The Final Dope."

Suggestions

When you move from one paragraph to another, place a bookmark where you are, then turn to the next number. Once at the new number, move your bookmark there. Otherwise, in the thrill of the chase, you might get lost by flipping to the wrong paragraph. You might also want to keep a bookmark at the map of Los Angeles at all times, since you'll need to turn back to it frequently during the game. You will find a thumb index at the beginning of each case to help you locate it easily. Review the Case Opening as often as you like during the play, but try not to leaf through the book to reread previously visited paragraphs. You might lose your place, for one thing, and some might even call it cheating.

Don't be frustrated if you do not correctly answer *all* the objectives. These cases are meant to be challenging, which is why the HARD-BOILED point system and ratings were developed. The key to HARD-BOILED is to *survive* a case, and then figure it all out.

If you don't feel like facing the mean streets alone, collaborate with a friend or two and play out a case together.

Or, for the ultimate challenge, play HARD-BOILED using just your noodle. You'll still need to keep track of your M–M–M points, of course, but rely on your memory for everything else. You never spotted Spade or Marlowe dragging composition paper and #2 pencils along on a case, now did you, pal?

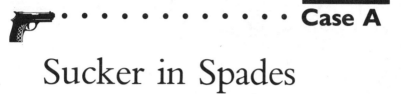 **Case A**

Sucker in Spades

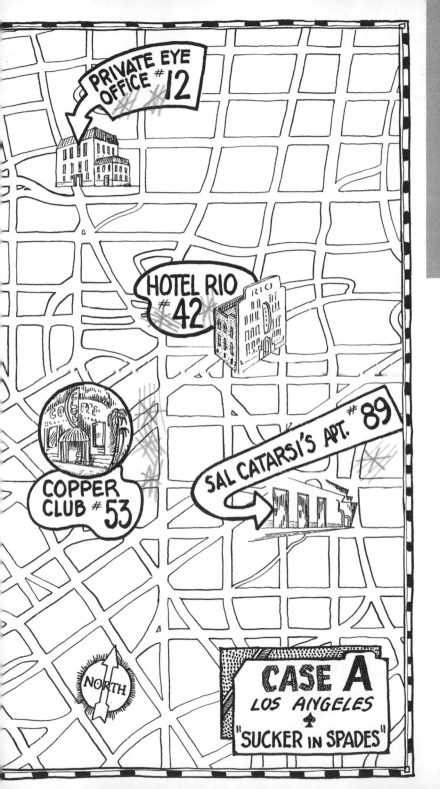

Objectives: 5

Difficulty: 🔋🔋🔋

M–M–M points: 125

Sucker in Spades

It's a busy day at the office. Dustballs gather around your shoes and you're watching the flies do barrel-rolls over your desk. Then a blonde walks in, a skinny little thing named Amanda Quincy. She's dressed like a minister's daughter—proper skirt and long-sleeved top with a neckline to her eyebrows. You sweat just looking at her. "This is no town for long sleeves, honey," you say. "L.A. thrives strictly on exposed flesh." But she looks drawn and distracted and joins the flies in ignoring you. She just sits down and tells you her story. There's always a story.

She's a Midwest girl—Illinois—and she's engaged to a salesman named Lance Farrell who came out here on business and sent for her later so they could get married. But when she arrived, Lance wasn't at the hotel. He wasn't anywhere. The cops were no help to her, which is no news to you. Then suddenly she got a note from Lance telling her to meet him at the Hotel Palm today at 4 o'clock. Room 18. She says she's afraid to go there alone. She feels something is wrong. So do you, but with nothing better to do you take the case. You say you'll meet loverboy yourself and ring her later. She runs down Lance's looks—tall, crewcut, twenty-five, a smooth talker who could sell you swampland with both your feet sunk to the ankles in muck. You think maybe he's in a real-estate scam. You try to think of someone in this town who isn't. You shrug and head for the Hotel Palm.

When you enter the Hotel Palm, you get hit with the smell of folded money. It's the kind of joint what puts chandeliers in the johns. You figure maybe Lance *did* make his California score, but he must be keeping on the q.t. because you find Room 18 registered under another handle—Simon Temperance. At his door, no one answers your knocks, so you grab the knob. It works, and the door springs open. Inside there's quite a layout. Fuzzy white rugs, windows that face the ocean, furniture made from wood older than your ties, which makes it pretty damn old. It'd be a swell place to stay if there wasn't a dead man laying all over the canopy bed. He's a fat-faced, bearded Johnny in pajamas, and by description definitely not Lance. He looks like he was strangled with the finesse of a professional. No sign of a struggle gives that hunch even more weight. You frisk his pants, which drape over a velvet chair.

In one pocket you find a matchbook from the Copper Club; in another, a post-office-box key. You spot a crumpled note with the name Sal Catarsi scribbled in red ink and with a shaky hand, as if Temperance was telling you who put the chill to him. But the whole thing smells like sardines in July. No pro would leave a body with a breath left in it, never mind a writer's itch. The phone book tells you Catarsi lives at 222 La Brea.

You pocket the note and call for the law. Then you call Amanda and tell her about Temperance. "You called the police, right?" she screams. "You called the police?"

"Sure," you say. "Relax, dreamboat. We'll find Lance on our own time." She says she'll be at the Regent Hotel if you need her. Then the cops walk in carrying sneers and shooting off questions. Your pal, Lt. Riker, wants to know everything. So you tell him everything. Well, everything except about Amanda and the Catarsi note. Let him work for the taxpayers' dough.

Objective #1: Where's Lance Farrell?

Objectives #2 and #3: Who killed Simon Temperance? Why?

Put a star (☆) next to:
 −the Copper Club
 −the Post Office
 −the Regent Hotel
 −Sal Catarsi's Apt.
 (Map for Case A on page 2−3).

#1 . "Down these mean streets a few good men must go."

Keep telling yourself that. Maybe it will stop you from thinking of how you should have gone to trade school like your old lady wanted.

(Throw the dice *one die at a time* and refer to the chart below to see which paragraph # you must go to.)

Street Chart

		1st die throw					
		1	2	3	4	5	6
2nd die throw	1	117	45	41	7	48	117
	2	23	117	96	82	74	10
	3	13	54	117	117	19	96
	4	96	118	117	117	70	79
	5	67	91	64	99	117	87
	6	117	96	29	58	96	117

#2   You confront her hard. She tries batting her lashes at you for effect. The breeze almost knocks you flat.
Subtract D + 3 Magnetism points.
NOW—if you still have *plus* (+) Magnetism points: Go to #14.
if you have *minus* (−) Magnetism points:
Roll the dice:
2–4 go to #78.
5–12 go to #14.

#3   The reference librarian is a brainy number with cheaters on and shapely measurements that have nothing to do with the Dewey Decimal system.

You go to her for assistance.
Go to #31.
or
You figure to stay clear of dames for awhile, especially ones with smarts, and you hit the newspaper stacks yourself.
Go to #90.

#4   You step out the door and run smack into a mean little badge, and it belongs to a mean little man—Lieutenant Riker, Homicide.

"See this piece of metal, shamus?"

It's hard to miss, considering he just about stuck it up your nose.

"It represents the law, shamus," he says. "Something you seem to skip over, kick around, trample on—everything but abide by."

"If I wanted to hear lectures, Lieutenant," you say, "I'd have gone to Harvard."

"I'll tell you where you *are* going, buddy-boy," he says.

He never does tell you. He figures you know by instinct. He's right. You could find your way downtown blindfolded. Unfortunately, you're not. You get to stare at his ugly puss all the way to the station house.

Go to #94.

#5   *Subtract D–2 Muscle points.*

You push the door in just when you think Carla's about to slam it on your shnozz. She flies back startled.

Go to #38.

#6   *Subtract D–5 Muscle points.*

You shoulder the door once and bounce off. The nosy nag snorts.

Subtract D–2 Muscle points.

You give it one more rush and crack through. You should have used the biddy as a door ram.

Go to #60.

#7   Your office rent is two months behind and your landlady is down the block looking for someone to sap with her broomstick—preferably you. You duck into the nearest gin joint until she passes.

Gain 10 Moxie points from downing a few ponies.

Go to (☆) location paragraph of your choice. See map.

#8   No answer again except from the nosy dame next door, natch. She's got a mudpack slapped on her mug and curlers twisting through what's left of her frayed gray hair. Medusa had nothing on this dame.

You decide to break Catarsi's door down.
Go to #6.
or
You woo Nosy into lending you a hairpin for some quick lockwork.
Go to #20.

#9   *Subtract D Moxie points.*
"Some strange guy downstairs says he got a package for Wilson. What should I do?" you say.

They look puzzled. "Tell him to beat it," says one with a jaw out to Toledo.

"Yeah," says the other, "We don't like no strangers here."

"That's what I figured," you say, and you close the door behind you. You wipe the sweat from your brow and thank God for inventing dunces.
Go to #32.

#10   Traffic is as congested as a three-pack-a-day Camel smoker in a steambath.
Subtract 3 points from the M–M–M column of your choice.
Go to (☆) location paragraph of your choice. See map.

#11   You're on the floor of Wilson's office like a loose sprawl of bones. You hear a ringing in your ears. You finally realize it was a phone because one of the broad-shouldered mugs is talking on it. The mug hangs up.

"Mr. Wilson wants we should take the tough guy here to the warehouse," he says. "Also, we gotta pick up Wilson's girlfriend at the house."

"Her again," says the other pugnose. "Married to a dish like Mrs. Wilson, too. What's the boss doin' fooling around with this other broad? She's a doper, ain't she?"

The first mug laughs. "She got her uses," he says. You try to feel for your legs so you can get up, but your head refuses and the floor gets colder and the pool is as black and inviting as ever.

Go to #86.

#12   No messages. You sit and put your dogs up for a breather and try to make some sense of it all. The phone buzzes under your feet. It's Amanda.

"I used to know an Amanda once," you tell her. "She was a swell client I had what lost her boyfriend, then lost her hotel room. And both in the same day. Here I thought I had it bad just losing my marbles."

She gets weepy and says she's been at the YWCA trying to reach you. She checked out of the Regent because Lance buzzed her and said the heat was plenty hot and she should blow out of there and meet him at the Hotel Rio, Room 40. She's still afraid. You still smell sardines. You feel like you're spinning on a broken record and the tune stinks besides. You say you'll meet her there later. Sometimes you're a real sap.

Cross out a star at the private eye office.
Put a star (☆) next to the Hotel Rio.
Roll the dice:
    2–7, 11, 12 go to #1.
    8–10 go to #4.

#13   Traffic is almost as heavy as John D. Rockefeller's money belt.

> *Subtract 3 points from the M—M—M column of your choice.*
> *Go to (☆) location paragraph of your choice. See map.*

#14   You ask her, "So where's Catarsi?"

She looks scared and says she doesn't know. You grab her by the shoulders and twist her toward you. You want the lowdown on Catarsi's dealings with Wilson.

> *Subtract D—3 Muscle or D—2 Magnetism points.*

She says, "Catarsi's been eyeing Wilson's number-one spot since we hit L.A." Then she gets tough and sneers at you with those great big lips of hers. "And he'll get there, too," she says. "Real soon." And she laughs hard in your puss.

"He's almost there already," she says.

"Almost," you say. You let her loose, tip your hat, and kiss her off.

> *Cross out a star at the Copper Club.*
> *Go to #1.*

#15   The phone rings and she jumps up like she sat on a snake.

"I'm expecting an important call." She looks for you to get up and blow.

"Guess you can stop counting the minutes," you say. You sit like your butt is glued to the divan. She takes herself into the bedroom. She doesn't look happy. You pick up the extension real quiet.

> *Subtract D Moxie points.*
> *Go to #107.*

#16　　The club is closed for the day. You recognize the mug playing lookout as one of the pinstriped quints that cracked your skull and put you on the fast train to Hopsville.

　　One good sap deserves another, you always say.
Go to #119.
or
Instead of the strong-arm, you try talking to the goons in simple sentences even Tarzan could pick up.
Go to #108.
or
You move down the side alley to check out any loose windows. A big blue Pontiac sits thirty yards down. You hope it's not loaded with guys holding quick heaters.
Go to #50.

#17　　You didn't blow fast enough. The law in the person of Lt. Riker and two flatfoots storm down the hallway and nab you. You ready yourself to slug the old broad if she says "goody." Lucky for her, she clams up. Unlucky for you, it's a trip downtown.
Go to #94.

#18　　You pull the rod from its cozy home. It's a .28-caliber number with an all-black handle. You hear a whoosh of air. It's the sound of a well-aimed vase heading for your noodle. You feel it split into pieces on the back of your head and you tumble forward. Carla walks toward your sprawled body. "Snooping bast—"

　　You black out and are spared the insult.
Subtract D Muscle points.
Go to #101.

#19   Your ex-wife grabs you on the street. You swear she's looking more and more like Mussolini every day. She sings the alimony blues, while you dig down hard for all the charm you can muster to get away.
Subtract 3 Moxie points.
Go to (☆) location paragraph of your choice. See map.

#20   *Subtract D–3 Magnetism points.*
You smile nice as she fingers her greasy curlers for a bobby pin. She hands one to you and you resist the temptation to dip it in boiling water first. The lock falls open with a few good jabs at the keyhole. It pays to rub noses with crooks and sharpies.
Go to #60.

#21   You spend lots of time getting your thumbs dirty on old daily newspapers. Finally the article you're rooting for turns up. It says a Ted Mooney got himself stuck in the slammer on big-time dope-dealing charges for eight years. The dope ring supposedly cleared out of Chicago and set up shop in L.A., with Mr. Big never even fingered. A photo next to the piece shows the obvious fall guy for the ring—Ted Mooney, alias Simon Temperance. He looked better in pajamas.
Cross out a star at the library.
Go to #1.

#22   You dive behind an antique dresser in the hallway and your .38 special snaps off two shots. A third shot finds its mark and a gunsel crumples to the floor. You rise up and feel a piece of lead pierce your side and split up a few ribs. A quick look and Wilson is at the doorway behind you holding a smoking rod. You forgot about him. You also forget how to breathe.

(You can start the case over on page 5.)

#23   All the swell-looking dames are really giving you the once-over lately—curvy blondes, dark-eyed brunettes, playful redheads. Maybe it's because you changed your shirt this month.

Add 10 Magnetism points.

Go to (☆) location paragraph of your choice. See map.

#24   *Subtract D + 4 Magnetism points.*

You kiss her hard. Your lips are having a swell time, but a watchful eye spots a bouncer in a distant corner and he's raising an eyebrow. As long as it's not a blackjack, you think.

She smiles, then hardens.

"My marriage to Mr. Wilson is strictly business," she says.

"That what *he* thinks, too?" you ask.

"I don't care what he thinks," she says. She bites the nape of your neck.

"I have some business to do," you say to her. She looks puzzled.

"Ever hear of a Simon Temperance?" you say.

Her curvy hot-coal figure stiffens, then cools like the hard edge of an icebox.

Go to #39.

#25   Wilson's house isn't the hardest to find. It sits up on a hill all lit up, and has only a half dozen more pillars than the Parthenon. You stash your Buick on a nearby road and leg it up the incline.

You go to the front door where two mugs are shooting the breeze.
Go to #110.
or
You go to the back door where a sexy kitchen maid is sashaying around the cutlery.
Go to #44.

#26   *Subtract D Moxie points.*
You ask the bartender who the redheaded dish was and if she fools around. You drool on his hairy paw for effect. The bartender wipes his hand on a napkin and says Mrs. Wilson fools around but not with mugs who breathe through their mouths.

"Does her hubby know about her cheating?" you ask.

"He suspects, and he don't like it much," he says, "but he fools around, too. The real kick in the pants is that *his* side piece is a doper."
Go to #68.

#27   The file has a batch of nothing. Just a load of old letters with Chicago postmarks. But at least you got hold of where Mr. Wilson lives—448 Mulholland.

Cross out a star at the Copper Club.
Put a star (☆) next to Leonard Wilson's house.
Go to #1.

#28   You come to the base of a staircase outside the room. Upstairs all the rooms look dark except one. Downstairs you hear voices from a room down a plushly carpeted hallway.

You go upstairs.
Go to #35.
or
You go down the hallway.
Go to #34.

#29   The cute waitress you've been seeing spots you on the street, and she's real sore you haven't called. You say you're on a case, but she gets on yours. You sweet-talk her with promises of Paradise and two tickets to the fights.

Subtract 3 Magnetism points.
Go to (☆) location paragraph of your choice. See map.

#30   The Copper Club is a dive with a new coat of paint, which makes it clean enough for the Board of Health and slimy enough to be real popular. The place is buzzing like hungry bees. You get introduced to some honey—a Mrs. Carla Wilson, the owner's wife. She's got the sleek line of an Olds convertible and hair like a hot red sunrise. She sips champagne and offers you a glass. And maybe more.

Her husband, Leonard Wilson, appears from his office, followed by five broad-shouldered mugs all dressed in floppy black hats and pinstriped suits. They look like the Dionne quints gone crooked. Wilson himself is a thin, hard man in his fifties whose face has more angles than features. You figure he wears a dark gray suit to make sure it's color coordinated with his complexion. He shakes your hand like he's using pliers, then shoots a stare to his wife that'd give a polar bear frostbite. He leaves the club. It was a hard welcome to sit through. Even harder on account of Carla's hand playing squeezebox with your kneecap. She says her lips feel hot. You figure you could either dunk her head in the champagne bucket or kiss her silly.

You think about it.

You use Muscle.
Go to #71.
or
You use Magnetism.
Go to #24.

#31   "I need help," you tell her.

Her eyes dart from her book to your swank trench and back to her book.

"You certainly do," she says. "The Salvation Army is two blocks down on the left."

You flash your card under her lenses. "Oh," she flusters, "really?" Her face reddens, then relaxes, and she licks her lips and smiles.

"Are you really a private eye?" she says.

Her horn-rims start to steam up. You figure that's a good sign.

Subtract D Magnetism points.
Go to #21.

#32   You glide down the hallway toward the sound of an angry voice.
    Go to #34.

#33   *Subtract D Muscle points.*
    "Get your grubby hands off the apron, Mac," the bartender says. He chops your hand away. "You want information?" he says. "Call the operator."

    You decide to apologize and act like a stupid drunk.
    Go to #26.
    or
    You pull the bartender down by the collar. His chin cracks against the bar. "I don't got change," you say.
    Go to #61.

#34   You sneak down the hallway near the master bedroom and stretch an ear over what sounds like Wilson yelling at someone: "None of this would have happened if the cops found the note you planted and made the arrest. You're *sure* you planted his name? You weren't—"
    You'd like to hear the rest of the show but some heavy footfalls tell you trouble is blowing your way.

    You blow the other.
    Go to #63.
    or
    You hold tight to hear some more and maybe see who else is inside.
    Go to #114.

#35   You tiptoe like a prima ballerina on eggshells up the stairs. At the only lighted doorway, you use your ears. You hear the sound of cards being shuffled.

You poke your nose in for a looksee.
Go to #51.
or
You turn around and head downstairs.
Go to #32.

#36   You rifle through a drawer or two and dig up lots of bills and perfume samples. You stick your mitt in the back and find the handle of a small-caliber gun. A phone gets hung up in the bedroom.

You get your mitt out of the drawer and leave.
Go to #72.
or
You keep digging.
Go to #18.

#37   You start slapping the old man silly but he starts to giggle like your knuckles are tickling his funny-bone. This plan takes the count.
Subtract D–3 Muscle points.
Go to #102.

#38   She walks toward the bar with a smile she must be renting from Betty Grable because her body is all nerves.
     "Don't you call a girl before you drop yourself in her apartment?" she says.
     "I lost my nickel," you say.
     "All you lost is your manners," she says. She paws a glass of scotch and hands it to you. "You

should try finding them sometime," she says. "People might even get to like you."

"I'd rather find my nickel," you say. She laughs, but not without a strange quiver in her voice.

You throw the hooch down your throat to gain strength.

Go to #69.

or

You put the drink aside, figuring it's a mickey.

Go to #80.

#39   She goes pale and lets out a muted gasp. She says she's been threatened a few times lately in letters from someone who signs them by that name.

"Not really signs them," she says. "All the words in the notes are cut out from newspapers, so I can't tell who did it."

"And you never knew a Simon Temperance?" you ask.

"No. Never," she says.

"What do they threaten?" you ask.

She pulls at her napkin and bites her lip. "They threaten to tell Leonard about my lover unless I pay a price," she says.

"I wouldn't think you'd care either way," you say.

"I wouldn't normally, but . . . " She stops, then says, "Those letters are driving me crazy."

You say she'll be getting less mail from now on.

She grabs your hand and says she wants you to come to her own private apartment sometime for a few drinks. "Sure," you say.

She has an appointment and leaves the club.

Put a star (☆) next to Carla Wilson's apartment.

You decide to shoot the breeze with the bartender.
Go to #43.
or
You sneak behind the bandstand to locate Leonard Wilson's office. It should be nice and vacated.
Go to #55.

#40 "Hey, Hart!" you yell.

Captain Hart jerks his head and tabs you being cuffed. He raises his hand and the blue boys stop squeezing you. So he remembers the time you fingered some toughs and gave *him* the headlines and the handshakes. He gets you off the hook with Riker. You tip your hat on the way out. Riker points his finger at you like it was a .38 ready to spring. "Next time," he says.

Go to #1.

#41 Your car says "Goodnight, Irene" smack in the middle of evening traffic. You had a hunch this would happpen when it started getting the heebie-jeebies three miles back.

Subtract 3 points from the M–M–M column of your choice.
Go to (☆) location paragraph of your choice. See map.

#42 You knock at Room 40 and Amanda opens the door. She is so glad to see you she whips out a .25-caliber pistol and points it at your heart. She looks like she's been hanging from her toenails over a dark bottomless pit, strung out. Her eyes are fixed on you, but looking through you—to Pluto, for all you can tell. She mutters something about your getting too close.

You use Muscle.
Go to #115.
or
You use Moxie.
Go to #105.

#43   You wander to the bar.

You act like a drunk on the make and ask who the redheaded dish was who left.
Go to #26.
or
You act like a hard guy and snatch the bartender's apron. You want some inside dope, you say.
Go to #33.

#44   The young kid of a maid gives you the once-over and you oblige.
Subtract D–1 Moxie points.
"I'm one of Wilson's new watchdogs," you say. Her eyes spark beneath her dark hair.
"Bow-wow," she says. She sits up on the kitchen counter and displays her black stockings like they're for sale at bargain prices.
Subtract D–1 Magnetism points.
You go to move past her. "I got to go protect the boss now," you say like you were shy. She's the one who's shy. Shy fifteen years your age.
"I knew Mr. Wilson liked them big and strong," she says, "but he never liked them this good-lookin'." Her eyebrows make like Groucho and leer. You make like Harpo and play dumb. Then you beat it to the living room.
Go to #103.

#45   This case is chewing up your insides. You need a stiff drink and a long sleep. Right now Sally Rand could knock you over with a feather or a blown kiss.

Subtract 3 Moxie points.
Go to (☆) location paragraph of your choice. See map.

#46   Roll the dice:
        2–6, 10 go to #83.
        7–9, 11, 12 go to #37.

#47   You go to grab the guard by his Buster Browns, but he's nimble. He does a skip, then comes down heel-first on three fingers. You yelp and yank back your wounded mitt.

"Don't try that again," the guard says, "or I *shoot* them off next time."

Subtract D–3 Muscle points.
Go to #102.

#48   You happen across Moose Mason on the street. You start to smile until you remember you sent this mug up the river five years ago for assault. He remembers too, and you and his blackjack get reacquainted.

Subtract 3 Muscle points.
Go to (☆) location paragraph of your choice. See map.

#49   The Copper Club is bouncing to the that boogie-woogie beat. So was your head the last time you were there. You see that the window to Wilson's office is dark.

You climb up on a garbage can and jimmy the window.

Go to #59.
or

You walk through the front door and get lost in the crowd. Then you go behind the bandstand and see if the hallway is deserted.

Go to #93.

#50   Luckily, the Pontiac is empty. You peep through a nearby window at the club and see that all the chairs except one are overturned on the tables. Carla Wilson sits there, her head on her hands, inhaling cigarettes like she was going underwater on each breath. You climb through the window.

Subtract D–5 Moxie points.

She is startled to see you.

Go to #2.

#51   You see two big boys playing poker with gats wrapped around their chests that could double for cannons. And swell luck, they see you, too.

You use Moxie.
Go to #9.
or
You use Muscle.
Go to #111.

#52   You've got to learn to hit harder. The bum on the floor snatches the heater from his belt and puts a slug in your chest. You touch the hole there like it was someplace else. In some wall. Made by some mouse maybe. Another slug in the side says, Wrong again. You're more like the cheese. Swiss. Over-aged and now, after a sudden hard headlong fall—very dead.

(You can start the case over on page 5.)

#53   At the Copper Club:
    if *no* stars are crossed out, go to #30.
    if *one* star is crossed out, go to #49.
    if *two* stars are crossed out, go to #66.

#54   You feel real good and real strong, like you could take on Jack Dempsey, your ex-wife, and Hitler— with both sets of knuckles tied behind your back.

Add 10 Muscle points.
Go to (☆) location paragraph of your choice. See map.

#55   The hallway is deserted. The big band out front drowns out your footfalls. You stop. A shadow appears from inside Wilson's office. You see the profile of a stone-faced gent checking out his knuckles like they're four baseballs that got sewn under his skin.

You decide hitting Wilson's office isn't worth the trouble.
Go to #43.
or
You see if you can't get the drop on this guard-dog.
Go to #73.

#56   Inside, all the chairs except one are overturned on the tables. Carla Wilson sits there, her head on her hands. She's smoking Camels and inhaling like she was going underwater on each breath.

Go to #2.

#57   *Subtract D–5 Muscle points.*

You grab your guard by his Buster Browns and pull. He crashes down like a fat tree and you pull the gun from his belt. Two shots into the lock and it springs open. Your guard's flapping feet tell you he's running for reinforcements. Your ancient roommate sits there bug-eyed and waves you bye-bye. Funny. Five years ago your ex-wife did the same thing, with almost as much emotion.

Go to #88.

#58   A big fat blonde in feathers and pumps swoops down on you and calls you a heel, flashing her blood-red fingernails like steak knives. Seems you finked on her loverboy awhile ago on some forgery scam. You give her the glad-eye, take her by the claw, and swear you'll make it up to her.

Subtract 3 Magnetism points.

Go to (☆) location paragraph of your choice. See map.

#59   *Subtract D–1 Moxie points or D–2 Muscle points.*

The window slips open easy and you slide into the pitch-dark office. You flick a match. The glimmer gives your hands direction—straight to the office records.

Go to #104.

#60   Catarsi's apartment is dark and quiet to the point of unease.

"Heard somebody come before," squawks Nosy, "but I wasn't presentable." You take another look at what she calls presentable. You force yourself. "I meant I was in the shower," she barks, "trying to dry off fast." You wish she'd dry *up* even faster.

A yellow light outlines the closed doorway to the bedroom. You call out Catarsi's name, pause, then flick the door open with a touch of your shoe.

Catarsi is inside, all right—only two .25-caliber bullets through his belly means he hasn't much to tell you and you can't even come back tomorrow when he's feeling better. The old broad stares with bright white eyes popping through black mud.

"Goody," she says.

You feel swell making an old lady's evening like this. You figure you'll take her to the morgue for Mother's Day. You call the law and let the mudhen supply the dope while you breeze off.

Objectives #4 and #5: Who killed Sal Catarsi? Why?

Cross out a star at Catarsi's apartment.
Go to #95.

#61   The bartender's eyes shoot to the right. A signal. His lips are clamped shut. Three of the broad-shouldered quints snatch you off his neck and pound you from both sides of your face. You slide down into a black pool.

Subtract D Muscle points.
Go to #11.

#62   It wasn't Hart. The blue boys throw you in a prowl car and make like a fire truck to the station house.

Go to #94.

#63   *Cross out a star at Wilson's house.*
Put a star (☆) next to:
    −your private eye office
    −the Copper Club.
Go to #1.

#64   You feel like hell. You have a three-day stubble on your face, a tongue as thick as a baloney, and bags under your eyes a bellhop wouldn't carry for less than a sawbuck.

Subtract 3 Moxie points.
Go to (☆) location paragraph of your choice. See map.

#65   "You're a bill collector, then?" she says. "Or better yet, the tax man."

You squeeze your eyes shut, then pop one open. You say you're the tax man.

"Goody," she says.

Subtract D Moxie points.
Go to #81.

#66   Roll the dice:
        2–8 go to #75.
        9–12 go to #16.

#67   Louie "Creeps" Malone, an ex-con and known fence, runs up to your car and says he needs a lift to the harbor. You tell him to buzz off. He sticks a .38 in your ear so you can hear better. You tell him to hop in and make himself cozy.
    Subtract 3 points from the M–M–M column of your choice, worrying about the time slipping from your mitts.
    Go to (☆) location paragraph of your choice. See map.

#68   As you leave, all five of Wilson's goons nab you and want to play catch with your skull. They tell you to lay off Carla Wilson and sap you good.
    Subtract D Muscle points.
    Go to #86.

#69   The booze tastes good and tingles your insides. You needed that.
    Add 10 points to the M–M–M column of your choice.
    Go to #15.

#70   You feel like a regular wiseguy lately, cracking off to anyone in earshot. You're backchatting to cabbies, hotel clerks; you're even calling your landlady "sister."
    Add 10 points to the M–M–M column of your choice.
    Go to (☆) location paragraph of your choice. See map.

#71   *Subtract D Muscle points.*
    You slap her hand away from your thigh.
    "I don't like being played the loverboy just so

your husband gets front-row-center seats to see the show," you say.

She crinkles her nose.

"My marriage to Leonard is strictly business," she says.

"At least from where *you're* sitting," you say. "I'm not sure your hubby would agree."

"Let's say I'm open for suggestions," she says. You cut off the approach of a caressing hand.

"And I'm closed for Arbor Day," you say. "Ever hear of a Simon Temperance?"

Go to #39.

#72   *Cross out* a star at Carla Wilson's apartment.
Put a star (☆) next to Catarsi's apartment.
Go to #1.

#73   You can't. The guy must have seen you in the reflection off his manicure. He swings around just as you raise your right fist. You're frozen for an instant, and doing a swell impersonation of the Statue of Liberty. He's not a big fan when it comes to charades and he flattens your nose. You thud when you hit the floor.
Subtract D Muscle points.
Go to #11.

#74   Your car says "Sayonara, Charlie" smack in the middle of noon traffic. You had a hunch this would happen when the piston heads started playing taps under the hood three miles back.
Subtract 3 points from the M–M–M column of your choice.
Go to (☆) location paragraph of your choice. See map.

#75   (If you were here at #75 before—go to #16.)

The Copper Club looks closed for the day. You press your nose to the entrance doorway and take a gander inside. Now you know why the joint is called the Copper Club. The place is crawling with them. Only one word pops into your head—amscray. No dice. Two back-up boys in blue grab you in the doorway. "Just the peeper we're looking for," says one, grinning. Inside, Lt. Riker sees you collared and sneers. "Take him downtown and see what he knows about how bodies and bullets meet up," he says.

"They call it murder," you say. You sound like the title to a lousy book.

"See?" says Riker. "He knows plenty." His face turns to stone. "Take him."

As they drag you out, you think maybe you spot Capt. Hart. He'd pull you from this jam.

Roll the dice:
    2–6 go to #40.
    7–12 go to #62.

#76   *Subtract D–3 Magnetism points.*

You sweet-talk the biddy about how she must've been a looker back when, and still is, with those fine eyes and upper-class nose. She blushes. Probably sticks that snoot through keyholes, you think, to catch a whiff of gossip.

"What about Catarsi?" you say.

Go to #81.

#77   *Subtract D Moxie points.*

You throw the few cups and chairs around and start pleading self-defense in a half-groggy voice like you were still doped up and the old guy's snapped and is taking it out on you. You scream real good. Unless the old guy turns out to be Howard Hughes out for a high time, the guard should realize you're the more valuable piece of merchandise in there.

Sure enough. He shouts outside like he's real concerned for your welfare. He unlocks the door and as he steps in you kick out your right foot. It lands in his belly. He drops his gun and a straight left hand drops him.

Subtract D Muscle points.

Your ancient roommate sits there bug-eyed and waves you bye-bye. Funny. Five years ago your ex-wife did the same thing, with almost as much emotion.

Go to #88.

#78   She grabs you and plants her ruby lips on your mouth. You're too weak to fuss. She holds you like there's no tomorrow. And there isn't.

A knife cuts through your back and you slump to your knees. She backs off sneering.

"I signalled you to deck him, not kill him," she yells.

"I needed the throwing practice," says another one of the quints from the hallway. "Still got a good eye, huh?"

A real good eye, you think. A bull's-eye. You fall over dead.

(You can start the case over on page 5.)

#79   Two coppers on patrol are tailing you so close they might as well sit in your trunk. You try to shake them.

Roll the dice:

2–3   You bust onto one of those ugly new freeways and get the law dizzy in a concrete pretzel they call a cloverleaf. *Add 5 points to the M–M–M column of your choice.* Go to (☆) location paragraph of your choice. See map.

4–6   You dodge into Fast Sammy's used-car joint. The cops can't spot your junkheap in with all the other junkheaps. Go to (☆) location paragraph of your choice. See map.

7–10   Can't shake them. *Subtract 2 points from the M–M–M column of your choice* (Throw dice again.)

11–12   Can't shake them. *Subtract 5 points from the M–M–M column of your choice* (Throw dice again.)

#80   "What's the matter?" says Carla. "I thought you were thirsty."

"Yeah," you say. "For info."

She grabs your glass and gulps it down.

"I don't like wasting good liquor on cheap snoopers," she says. "No offense."

"I'm hard to insult," you say.

"I'm *not.* You thought I slipped something in your drink, didn't you?"

"It crossed my mind, knowing your associates," you say. She looks like a wounded cat. A wildcat.
Go to #15.

#81 She says Catarsi's a real no-gooder, a piece of scum acting like cut diamonds who's some kind of assistant manager of a nightclub downtown. A place where they drink a lot, she's sure. You nod. Worst of all, he drags this redheaded dish up to his apartment all the time, and on the sly, too. "God knows what they do," she says. You nod. "He's not home," she says, "but you find him and get him good." You nod, bow, and get the hell out of there.
Cross out a star at Catarsi's apartment.
Go to #1.

#82 You look real spiffy. Your pants have only a few less wrinkles than those leatherskin cronies who read dime novels at the beach, and your trenchcoat looks like you slept in it for a month. It's only been a week and a half.
Subtract 3 Magnetism points.
Go to (☆) location paragraph of your choice. See map.

#83 You start slapping the old man around and he starts screaming like an old lady. It's a high-pitched squawk that would deafen a Great Dane. The guard outside starts yelling too, real concerned. He unlocks the door and as he steps in you kick out your right foot. It lands in his belly. He drops the gun, and a straight left hand drops him. You take a powder at the door.
Subtract D Muscle points.
Go to #88.

#84   Roll the dice:
        2–4 go to #57.
        5–12 go to #47.

#85   *Subtract D Magnetism points.*

"Got a drink for a dumb but handsome gum-shoe?" you ask. You spread your lips and flash every tooth in your head.

"Sure," she says. You step inside.

Go to #38.

#86   When you come to, you realize you've been doped up all day. You have a cotton swab for a head and your arms suffer from needlepoint in a black-and-blue design. Your room is part of an abandoned warehouse and makes Skid Row look like Park Place and Boardwalk. It's damp and made of stone. The door is solid except for a flap-hole at the bottom where they can shove in some grub if you're a good boy and don't bark too loud. You even got a roommate.

He's an old, small, ratty man with eyes glazed over like a nickel doughnut. You check out his arm, but he yanks it away and rolls down his sleeves to hide his marks. They all want to hide their marks. He keeps talking about how he'd do anything for some hop and he picks at his navel. This tea-party chatter gets you restless. You say, "The name Lance Farrell mean anything to you, buddy?" Nothing. The geezer just drools. The name Joe DiMaggio would get the same puddle for an answer.

Go to #102.

#87 Some mug is tailing you. He's your average-looking hard guy, not quite as tall as the Chrysler building. You feel frisky and confront him. He bounces a blackjack off your head.

   Subtract 3 Muscle points.
   Go to (☆) location paragraph of your choice. See map.

#88 You dodge through what seem like endless wooden crates and you hear the rumble of voices behind you, then shouts. You jump through an open window. You hit the alleyway and roll. You get up and wince at the steamy glare of the California sun.

   Cross out a star at the Copper Club.
   Put a star (☆) next to the Copper Club.
   Go to #1.

#89 At Catarsi's Apt.:
    if *no* stars are crossed out, go to #112.
    if *one* star is crossed out, go to #8.

#90   You never *were* good with numbers, unless you include taking the ten count when getting slugged. Maybe using the glasses dame wouldn't have been such a bad idea. This bookworm routine is for the birds.

> *Subtract D–2 Muscle and D–2 Moxie points.*
> Go to #21.

#91   Your car says "Adios, Muchachos" smack in the middle of morning traffic. You had a hunch this would happen when the engine started doing the rumba three miles back.

> *Subtract 3 points from the M–M–M column of your choice.*
> Go to (☆) location paragraph of your choice. See map.

#92   You open up the P.O. box with your key and find a logbook keeping money records, money going to a Ted Mooney from Leonard Wilson. *Big* money. The name Mooney rings a bell. Something about a newspaper story and dope. You figure to do some research sometime at the library.

> *Cross out* a star at the Post Office.
> *Put a star* (☆) next to the Public Library.
> Go to #1.

#93   *Subtract D Moxie points.*
You breeze through the joint like you owned it. Lucky for you the barman from last time got the night off. The hallway is empty and the door to Wilson's office opens with a twist of the knob. Once inside, you flick a match. The glimmer gives your hands direction—straight to the office records.

> Go to #104.

#94   In the interrogation room they grill you good. They keep calling you "pally" and siccing some lug with long nasal hairs on you. Give these badges credit. They play rough and know where it hurts.

Subtract one die roll from your weakest M–M–M column.

They got nothing to hold you on except maybe three counts of exposing facial stubble on public property. They toss you out on the seat of your trench.

Go to #1.

#95   Roll the dice:
2–4, 10 go to #17.
5–9. 11, 12 go to #1.

#96   You stop in at a local joint and buy a bottle of good hooch to give you that extra pep. Besides, you couldn't think of anything else for dinner.

Add 10 points to the M–M–M column of your choice.
Go to (☆) location paragraph of your choice. See map.

#97   Your nose is sinus-deep in Wilson's file drawer when some lug comes in and surprises you. You get mad because you should have smelled this gorilla's breath from Long Beach. Luckily, you surprised *him* by being there in the first place. You lay him out with a good right hand.

Subtract D Muscle points.

NOW—if you still have *plus* (+) Muscle points: Go to #27.
if you have *minus* (−) Muscle points:
Roll the dice:
2–4 go to #52.
5–12 go to #27.

#98   You surprise Carla at the door. She's wearing a lavender silk robe with blue feathers flying around her neck.

> You use Muscle.
> **Go to #5.**
> *or*
> You use Magnetism.
> **Go to #85.**

#99   You run into ex–Detective Sergeant Murphy, a crooked cop from way back who's pounding a beat now instead of serving time like he oughtta. You crack wise about his feet getting flatter, so he saps you for the exercise.
Subtract 3 Muscle points.
Go to (☆) location paragraph of your choice. See map.

#100   You pin her to the floor until she spills some news. She says she didn't kill Mooney. All she admits to is that she planted the Catarsi note at the Hotel Palm and used you to be sure the cops would show and find it. Then she passes out. You give her a break and don't roll up her sleeves.
Cross out a star at the Hotel Rio.
Go to #1.

#101   You find yourself propped up in a sitting position out in the hallway. You shake off the fuzz and wobble down the carpet. You hear voices. They sound like cops steaming up the stairs. You haul those dogs of yours out a hallway window and down the fire escape.
Go to #72.

#102   You've got to lam out of this nightmare of a dope factory. But how?

Reach your hand out the bottom flap so you can yank the feet of your guard and snatch the gun from his belt.
Go to #84.
or
Beat the daylights out of the old man so his screams bring the guard inside.
Go to #46.
or
Pretend the old guy has gone batty and is beating you.
Go to #77.

#103   The living room is empty, though a lot of fancy portraits are staring at you and giving you the willies. Dead right is a room stacked with more books than the public library. Must be Wilson's study, you figure.
Go to #106.

#104   Roll the dice:
2–8 go to #97.
9–12 go to #27.

#105   *Subtract D Moxie points.*

You tell Amanda she needs help. Funny thing to say since she ain't the one with a .25 automatic aimed at her navel. You tell her you have some stuff for her. Good stuff. Pure stuff. Stuff that dreams are made of. But she's got to put the heater down, you say, or else no deal.

She nods and starts to cry, then drops the muzzle just a hair. You slap the gun from her hand.

Go to #100.

#106   *Subtract D–2 Moxie points.*

You work your way into Wilson's drawers and root through his files like a desperate mutt looking for a prize bone. This time there's paydirt. You find lots of scrap paper in Wilson's handwriting. They're rough drafts of the letters sent to Wilson's wife from "Temperance." Underneath sit a few stacks of newspapers with lots of letters clipped out and used to make the originals. You ease the file drawer shut.

Go to #28.

#107   A man's voice says, "Rest easy, babe. It's done. He won't be putting no squeeze on us anymore, 'cause I put the squeeze on him." Carla says that Leonard might still suspect, that he suspects a lot of things, that talk's going around.

"Nix on the talk," the man says. "Talk's good for hot air. Besides, Wilson don't like to dirty his hands."

She says, "Yeah, but I've seen him dirty other people's hands while they were doing *his* work."

While he tries to calm Carla down, you ease the phone back on the hook.

You slip out the door.
Go to #72.
or
You rummage through a few drawers.
Go to #36.

#108   *Subtract D Moxie points.*

You lower your hat over your eyes. You flip a badge at the mug and say "Board of Health." You say you need to inspect the kitchen. The mug nods, then juts his chin out a mile and a half.

"You look familiar," he says.

You say, "Some people think in a certain light I look like Jimmy Cagney." The mug puts his hand in his pocket. He ain't buyin'.

"In a different light I look like Rita Hayworth," you say.

"No kiddin'," he says. "You just look like a private snooper to me."

"That's only when there's no light at all." Your right hooks his jaw before he can pull the rod from his pocket, and he falls.

"See?" you say.
Subtract D Muscle points.
Go to #56.

#109   Amanda Quincy checked out, says the desk clerk at the Regent Hotel. No forwarding address. Swell.

Cross out a star at the Regent Hotel.
Go to #1.

#110   One of the heavies gets called to the garage. The other gets your knee at the base of his spine, then a fistprint up the side of his face.

Subtract D + 2 Muscle points.

You slide him behind a pillar and slip inside the house.

Go to #103.

#111   *Subtract D + 3 Muscle points.*

You grab the poker table quick and flip it into one goon's lap. The other you crack across the cheek with a backhand swipe. Both are resting comfortably. You listen for anybody outside. Nothing. You head downstairs.

Go to #32.

#112   You knock on his door and his neighbor, an old nosy dame, opens hers. Maybe if you knocked on her door Catarsi would open his. She gives you the once-over and snaps her head in approval.

"About time," she says. "About time that immoral beast got his."

"Got his what?" you ask playfully. She straightens up and jerks her housecoat.

"What's comin' to him," she snarls. "And I hope it's a fistful of knuckles and a set of busted choppers. And a good poke in the belly on the side."

"Want to hold the mashed-in nose?" you say. "Or was that busted ribs to go?" She clams up and jerks her coat again. "I'm no bruiser take-out service, lady," you say. "I'm just looking for Sal Catarsi. You seen him?"

"Maybe," she says coyly.

You use Moxie.
Go to #65.
or
You use Magnetism.
Go to #76.

#113   *Subtract D Muscle points.*
The bruiser is leaning on the wall daydreaming. Out of sight, you flip some coins high in the air and they land at his feet. The goon looks up like the Big Cheese in the sky is finally coming through with the payoff. He bends over and you kick him good and hard. He nose-dives to the pavement. Then you kick the other end of his body, the one with the nose stuck on it. You leave the coins next to his limp hand. The mug earned the tip.

Go to #56.

#114   *Subtract D Moxie points.*

Wilson's voice becomes muffled but the shadow of the other person moves closer. A bullet zips past your ear like the whisper of death. You'd better blow but fast.

NOW—if you still have *plus* (+) Moxie points: Go to #116.

if you have *minus* (–) Moxie points:

Roll the dice:

2–9 go to #116.

10–12 go to #22.

#115   *Subtract D–2 Muscle points.*

You duck. She fires high, and you slap the gun from her hand.

Go to #100.

#116   Go to #63.

#117   You blow through red lights plenty fast, hoping the coppers are eyeing sidewalk nylons or taking siestas, two of the three things they're real good at. The other is breaking your chops whenever possible.

Go to (☆) location paragraph of your choice. See map.

#118   Some dumb gunsel has been following you for blocks, probably holding a gat and a grudge. You try to shake him fast.

Roll the dice:

2–3   Can't shake him. *Subtract 5 points from the M–M–M column of your choice. (Throw dice again.)*

4–7   Can't shake him. *Subtract 2 points from the M–M–M column of your choice. (Throw dice again.)*

8–10   You duck into Wang Lee's laundry and hide behind the dirty towels. The gunsel loses you. You throw a few yen to Wang for the consideration. Go to (☆) location paragraph of your choice. See map.

11–12   You turn on the gunsel in an alley and flatten his nose for him. *Add 5 points to the M–M–M column of your choice.* Go to (☆) location paragraph of your choice. See map.

#119   *Subtract D–3 Muscle points.*

You bop him from behind but good.

Go to #56.

Hard-Boiled Points (Case A) (205 pts.)

Objective #1: There is *no* Lance Farrell.   __10__ points

Objectives #2 and #3: Sal Catarsi *actually*
killed Simon Temperance (Ted Mooney) . . .   __40__ points
    . . . because Catarsi thought that Tem-
perance was blackmailing Carla and him (al-
though it was really Wilson who wrote those
letters to his wife).   __60__ points
    —Leonard Wilson had Simon Temper-
ance killed through an unsuspecting Catarsi
(and then tried to implicate him with Amanda's planted note) . . .   __10__ points
    . . . because Temperance was blackmail-
ing Wilson about the Chicago drug ring.
(Temperance was probably threatening to
reveal information that would destroy the
operation now that it had moved to L.A.)   __20__ points

Objectives #4 and #5: Amanda (Wilson's mis-
tress) *actually* killed Sal Catarsi . . .   __35__ points
    . . . because the planted note failed to lead
to Catarsi's arrest. (You snatched it from the
body before the police could find it. In other
words, the first plan failed, and Amanda had
to do the job personally this time or suffer
Wilson's rage.)   __10__ points
    —Wilson had Catarsi killed through a
drugged Amanda . . .   __5__ points
    . . . because Catarsi was having an affair
with his wife *and/or* was trying to take over
the ring himself.   __15__ points

Hard-Boiled Rating (Case A)

145–205 points . . . . One Tough Egg

85–140 points . . . . Gumshoe with Guts

45–80 points . . . . Soft-Boiled Shamus

0–40 points . . . . Near-Sighted Peeper

The Final Dope (Case A)

At the station house, the law puts you on the grill. They always like the smell of a private dick sizzling.

"Listen, boys," you say, "you're forgetting something. I'm not the hophead what ventilated Catarsi. That's the blonde with the gopher holes running up her arm. I'm the good guy. Check me out. Trench, fedora—"

"Skip the fashion show," says Lieutenant Riker. Riker is an honest cop, but he likes you like he likes the holes in his socks. You wish he'd stop sucking on his stogey when he talks to you. Maybe he'll even light it one of these weeks. Better yet, swallow it.

"What about this note business?" he asks. "Seems it was an easy plant we never got to pluck, if you get my meaning."

You love it when a cop goes poetical on you.

"I swiped it," you say, "on account of I was protecting my client. Like I told you, I figured that it was an obvious set-up. That somebody like Leonard Wilson or maybe Lance Farrell bumped off Temperance and was hanging the frame on Catarsi. At least, that's how a frame-up usually runs. The killer leaves a note blaming some sucker. But in this case, the sucker *was* the killer, and the set-up was Wilson's and it kept him miles away and clean. He likes to be untouchable. He practices a lot."

"We're gonna touch him, all right," says Riker. "We're gonna more than touch that bird. We're gonna throw him in the jug for good. You better believe it."

"I believe it," you say. "I also believe in the tooth fairy and Santy Claus." After two more hours, they get sick of listening to your chatter and let you go.

A few weeks later, you hear that Carla Wilson skipped on her hubby down to Mexico somewhere. Just what they need down there, another fiery redhead. Amanda got the fits in cold turkey and snapped. She never went to trial. She's in with the white-coats sewing purses for the Women's League and wearing slippers all the time. Yeah, and Wilson . . . you hear he moved the operation to Miami. You remember how you once, a million years ago, believed there was a Santy Claus. Then again, about a month ago, you believed there was a Lance Farrell.

You take a long nap.

THE END
(Case A)
"SUCKER IN SPADES"

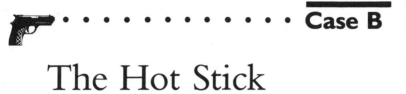

Case B

The Hot Stick

Objectives: 7

Difficulty: 🔫🔫🔫

M–M–M points: 145

The Hot Stick

Some lucky Joes get greeted in the morning by birds cheeping their lungs out from a tree outside. *You* get some bum climbing through the garbage cans in the alley next door. What really gets you sore is that he always finds suits better-looking than yours. One morning you hit your office and another one of these ragheaps is going through a trash bin you call your desk. "Hey, bub, what gives?" you say, and the heap turns around. His face surprises you. It's strong-featured and has a lot of smarts for an old geezer.

"Perusing your credentials," he says, and he holds up your best blackjack. "You judge a man by his things. See? This tells me you got the courage and the character." Then he hoists an ashtray, full of butts, doing a pretty swell impersonation of Mt. McKinley. "This tells me you're a slob," he says.

You figure he hasn't bumped into a mirror of late.

But he shrugs it off and pops a fancy card in your mitt. Gold scribbles say *"Coley and Son, Antiques—Irving Coley, Prop."* Only then do the rags fit—he's old, he's rich, he's cheap. His face wrinkles like a Polish accordion and burns red. "I was robbed!" he shouts, and you hear about some silver candlestick-holder, half of a pair of them, that got snitched from his shop last night to the tune of eight grand, and he wants you should nose it out for him. "What about the law?" you ask. "Pah!" he says, "I'd be dropped and dead before I got through the complaint forms. Paper-pushing punks, they are!"

You smile. He's your kind of old geezer.

So you drive to the shop while he spills the whole set-up. Says he took inventory last night from 5:00 to 8:00 and both candlesticks were alive and kicking. Then he sacked out upstairs while his son, Sampson, worked over some numbers in the back office and his grandson, Ansel, cleaned up. Next morning, Old Coley noticed a jimmied back window and, sure enough, a silver stick got restless and walked.

"Dropping a filling worth eight G's," you say, "makes your teeth hurt." "Mister," Coley snorts, "my whole body hurts."

Before you walk into the shop, Coley stops and shoots you a sharp line about his grandson. "Kid's a little disturbed," he says. "Got some problems. Goes to a special school downtown, Greely's." No big deal. His eyebrow twists up like a hard gray worm that says, Lay off.

Sampson Coley drags out of the back room. He looks beat. He's middle-aged and has thick glasses and small, dark eyes. His shoulders droop like seven continents, the Angel of Death, and Kate Smith sat on top of them. He rehashes yesterday, how he did some personal deliveries after 5:00 P.M., then sat in the park at 6:00 and read till 8:00 like he always does in the summer. Later, he worked on the account books in the back office till at least 10:00, he thinks, 'cause he was on the phone for an hour from 9:00 on. Then he took his kid and went upstairs to bed. "And your wife?" you ask. "She's dead," he snaps. Old Coley's puss goes white and he leaves. Young Coley says his marriage was for the birds, especially after Ansel was born. "Nothing like having a vegetable for a sonny-boy," he says, "to do in a marriage for keeps."

This guy's a real sweetheart. You'd like to readjust his nose, but you hold off.

You spot the kid, Ansel, in the corner. A big-eyed, teen-aged pup, all arms and legs, sweeping up the floor. "That's all he does," says Young Coley, "day and night. Don't know nothing about nothing." The kid stares at you like you got three heads or he saw your ex-wife. He gives you the willies.

The old guy comes back in with the other stick to show you. It's a beaut, all right—heavy silver, about a foot high, with white satin cushioning the bottom. "Why nab just one stick?" you ask, " Why nothing else?" "You're the dick," Young Coley smirks. "Gotcha, pal," you crack, "but I ain't no swami. I need a lead!"

Old Coley gives his wrinkles another workout and spits out a name—Cranston Banks. He's a rival collector with a shop on Melrose. He's wanted the sticks for awhile, but no sale. "Maybe he took them for spite," the geezer says. "He's hated our lot and the feeling's mutual. I'd kill that bum if I had the chance and he'd do likewise. That a good enough lead for you?"

"Yeah," you say, flicking your butt into some funny Chinaman's vase, "for a murder."

Objectives #1 and #2: Who took the silver candlestick-holder from the store? Why?
Put a star (☆) **next to:**
    —Greely's Special School
    —Banks's Antiques.
    (Map for case B on page 52–53.)
Go to #1.

#1   This case hits you like a breath of fresh smog. You're ready to choke on the name Coley, and the street offers no respite to a weary gumshoe. You hitch up your pants and keep moving.

      (Throw the dice *1 die at a time* and refer to the chart below to see which paragraph # you must go to.)

Street Chart

	1st die throw					
	1	**2**	**3**	**4**	**5**	**6**
1	117	45	41	7	48	117
2	23	117	96	82	74	10
3	13	54	117	117	19	96
4	96	118	117	117	70	79
5	67	91	64	99	117	87
6	117	96	29	58	96	117

(Row labels "2nd die throw" at left)

#2   *Add D–4 Moxie points.*

Outside the brunette looks bored. Banks holds up
five fingers and sticks them in her mug. The brunette
shrugs. You make out the word "delivery" from
Banks's fat lips. The brunette turns and blows down
the street. Meanwhile, Banks looks like someone gave
him the word that his toupee came off of some dead
poodle.

He returns and you tell him about Coley and the
stick that got loose.

Go to #5.

#3   From a corner booth, you try calling Francine White like you've been doing all day, and you get the same story—no answer. Inside the shop, Sampson Coley's beating on Ansel for breaking this old flowered drinking cup only some granny would want to slap her lips on. Sampson's hot 'cause the kid played mum about it till he found the pieces under a piano bench this afternoon. You poke your snoot in to stop the fisticuffs. The kid scuffles off and you ask Sampson who he was yakking with on the phone for an hour the night of the robbery. "Lyle Skelling," he says, "What's it to you? You know him?"

"Let's say I ran into a fist he owns that goes by the handle of Ace," you say.

You don't get a chance to read the look on Young Coley's face, 'cause a hoarse shriek comes from the side alley.

Go to #9.

#4   At Banks's Antiques:
> if *no* stars are crossed out, go to #16.
> if *one* star is crossed out, go to #65.
> if *two* stars are crossed out, go to #69.

#5   Banks backs up Old Coley's story about them being business rivals, his being interested in the silver sticks, and his being told to take the air. Says he keeps special two collections—candlestick-holders and music boxes. You pick up a box with a porcelain ballerina perched on top looking sweet and graceful and like no frail you ever met in Mooney's Bar & Grill.

"Oh, yeah," you say. "When you pop one of these numbers open it starts tooting 'Take Me Out to the Ballgame' or something."

Banks grinds his dentures. Like big fat clams,

these kinds of Johnnies open up when you get them steamed.

"Just like the Coleys," he growls, "to employ a shamus as ignorant and as vile as they are. They have stubbornly refused to sell me their silver pieces. Rather, they hold them for spite. Those oafs might as well be selling plumbing fixtures. They have neither the appreciation nor the finesse for fine furnishing."

"They ain't handing you any door prizes either," you say, and you hit the street.

Cross out a star at Banks's Antiques.
Put a star (☆) next to your private eye office.
Go to #1.

#6   Subtract D Muscle points.

Tattino may be a big nothing now, but he's such a good Joe. He's telling you everything you're asking about, and all just because you got your elbow jammed in his throat. What a pal!

Go to #8.

#7   Your office rent is two months behind and your landlady is down the block looking for someone to sap with her broomstick—preferably you. You duck into the nearest gin joint until she passes.

Gain 10 Moxie points from downing a few ponies.
Go to (☆) location paragraph of your choice. See map.

#8   The Squid talks low and raspy and says, "Skelling runs a real sweet racket. He gives jewelry and antique dealers the word to spread some trinkets his way, so he can ship the stuff down to Mexico for *mucho dinero*. In return, he gives the shops 'protection.'"

"What's he do?" you ask. "Promise not to send Ace to visit when it's feeding time?"

"Yeah," Vito gurgles, still barely over a whisper, "something like that."

"You should do something for your throat, Vito," you say. "You sound like hell." You detach your elbow from his Adam's apple and blow.

Cross out a star at the Ex-Racketeer.
Put a star (☆) next to Banks's Antiques.
Go to #12.

#9   Out the side door, and who's there but your morning rooster—alias the neighborhood bum with the expanding wardrobe. His eyes are popping out of his skull, his mouth is as wide as the Lincoln Tunnel, and in his right hand he holds a shoe he pinched. Too bad the shoe's still got a foot in it, with a leg that runs down into the heap of garbage in the big trash bin. It's some poor mug's body whose face is so bashed in his mother wouldn't know him from the Crown Prince of Baghdad. No I.D. on him, either. The bum shakes his trance and starts beating his feet down the alley.

You chase him.
Go to #35.
or
You let him go for now.
Go to #89.

#10   Traffic is as congested as a three-pack-a-day Camel smoker in a steambath.

Subtract 3 points from the M–M–M column of your choice.
Go to (☆) location paragraph of your choice. See map.

#11   Roll the dice:
          2–6 go to #40.
          7–12 go to #80.

#12   On the way out one of the dockside lugs who saw you rough Tattino up gives you the eye and calls you over. You're not sure whether he's going to slug you or congratulate you.

      You figure you'll see what he wants.
Go to #111.
or
You go to the phone to try Francine White's place again.
Go to #53.

#13   Traffic is almost as heavy as John D. Rockefeller's money belt.
Subtract 3 points from the M–M–M column of your choice.
Go to (☆) location paragraph of your choice. See map.

#14   *Subtract D–3 Moxie points.*
You land flat on your back near the chunks of glass from the vase that got broken. You work a piece in your hand and saw away at the rope around your wrist. At the end of a five-minute sweat you spring loose, just as footsteps sound on the other side of the door. Hard footsteps. Footsteps that mean business. You climb out the window. You're not in the mood for company.
Go to #18.

#15   You walk inside your waiting room and see somebody dumped a present for you. Francine White's body lies across one of your cracked leather chairs. Her mouth and eyes are open and lifeless. You check her purse. Her .22 rests inside. Seems she got one off, wherever she was, before the deadly reply. Her wallet spills out and open. Her I.D. shows the name Francine White Coley. You figure Sampson was right after all. His wife *is* dead. Guess if you wish hard enough . . .

     You cringe as you lift the receiver to call the law. You can't wait to see their smiling faces.

     Objectives #6 and #7: Who killed Francine White Coley? Why?

     Cross out a star at your private eye office.
     Go to #1.

#16   Banks's Antiques is a gingerbread house shoved in a smog-bank of cheap motels and liquor stores. Even the front door chimes like some Tinkerbell saying, "How's trix?" To top it off, Tink's chubby kid brother is behind the counter wearing a pucker for a smile. His wrists are thin and his hair is puffy and blond. He's the kind of guy what looks good in puce. He says Mr. Banks isn't around, but you see some dark-haired dame in the back and a man's arm in a pink ruffled shirt.

You think you'll apply some muscle to this quail.
Go to #31.
or
You tell him you're from the vice squad and watch his pucker melt.
Go to #77.

#17   *Subtract D Magnetism points.*

Her moniker is Francine White. She works at Skelling Shipping Company, a small exporting firm in the Palm Vista section. She hands you a picture of a man—around forty—Roman nose, smirky smile. He wears a swell pink suit. She says that Zack Kelley, who's a foreman down at the company, has been missing since day before last, and she's worried about her "associate."

"How close do you . . . associate?" you ask.

She looks ready to flip her scotch in your puss, but she doesn't. What she does is get real tough and real red, like her blood shot to her face and eyes and wanted out.

"Look, buster," she snaps, "I suspect things and I'll pay for some dope about him, but without the lip service. Got me? Then I'll do the rest."

You figure nothing bad should happen to this Mr. Zack Kelley or his pretty pink suit, or someone's taking a hard fall from a real hard filly.

Objective #3: Where is Zack Kelley?
Cross out a star next to your private eye office.
Put a star (☆) next to the Skelling Shipping Company.
Go to #1.

#18   *Cross out* a star at Lyle Skelling's house.
Put a star (☆) at Skelling Shipping Co.
Go to #1.

#19   Your ex-wife grabs you on the street. You swear
she's looking more and more like Mussolini every
day. She sings the alimony blues, while you dig down
hard for all the charm you can muster to get away.
Subtract 3 Moxie points.
Go to (☆) *location paragraph of your choice. See map.*

#20   You wait in a schoolroom like you waited for
weekly detention a few centuries back. A Miss Amy
Watson walks in and she's a knockout of a brunette
with her hair in a bun and her nose packed with freck-
les. The "weird" kids' classes always got the pretty
teachers. Lugs like you got Miss Pilkin with warts
hanging off her. You think you ought to close your
trap before you dribble like a hungry chimp. You in-
troduce yourself and grin.
Go to #126.

#21   *Subtract D Moxie points.*
From just outside the living room, you hear low
angry sounds coming from Skelling. "I was waiting," he says. "Waiting and waiting. Listening for it.
For at least an hour. Keeping him on the line. Letting
that punk curse me out just so I could hear it happen.
But nothing happened. What the hell went wrong?"
Another male voice asks something about, "Do
you want a second go-around or what?"
Skelling snaps, "No can do. Gotta cool our heels
some. Gotta nose out what fell apart first and how
that private dick ties in."

Before you can take a bow, you hear noise heading your way.

Go to #124.

#22   You pile through Banks's desk drawer. The Luger no longer resides there, but the shipping order does. It's a big order, five shipments' worth, this time just for silver antiques, Mexican dough up front, and the load's going bon voyage at 10:00 P.M. from Carson Docks. You glance at your watch—9:30 P.M.

Two sounds always turn your gut. One is the sound of a rod's click when it's ready to spit a bullet. The other is the spit. Lucky for you, you only hear the first. You whirl and see Banks coming out of a dark storeroom you never spotted, and he's holding his Luger real tight.

NOW—if you still have *plus* (+) Moxie points: Go to #55.

   if you have *minus* (–) Moxie points:
      Roll the dice:
         2–4 go to #38.
         5–12 go to #55.

#23   All the swell-looking dames are really giving you the once-over lately—curvy blondes, dark-eyed brunettes, playful redheads. Maybe it's because you changed your shirt this month.

Add 10 Magnetism points.
Go to (☆) location paragraph of your choice. See map.

#24   Your foot feels like it got itself stuck in a vat of cement. Ace grabs you by the ankle and twists you on top of Skelling's desk. Skelling decides he doesn't like you as a paperweight and bangs your head with his desk lamp. You go out cold.

Subtract D + 3 Muscle points.
Go to #98.

#25   At Skelling Shipping Company:
               if *no* stars are crossed out, go to #113.
               if *one* star is crossed out, go to #78.

#26   Roll the dice:
               2–8 go to #109.
               9–12 go to #24.

#27   At Coley Antiques:
               if *no* stars are crossed out, go to #3.
               if *one* star is crossed out, go to #76.

#28   You move down to the front of the house. You hear the distant rumble of gravelly voices and smell the sharp odor of nickel cigars.
        Go to #21.

#29   The cute waitress you've been seeing spots you on the street, and she's real sore you haven't called. You say you're on a case, but she gets on yours. You sweet-talk her with promises of Paradise and two tickets to the fights.
        Subtract 3 Magnetism points.
        Go to (☆) location paragraph of your choice. See map.

#30   Max says the man in the trash bin died of a smashed skull. You say, "And here I thought his face got caught in the path of a runaway egg-beater."
        "I'm eatin', for Pete's sake," says Max.
        "Well, stop eatin'," you say, "and start givin'. Something I *don't* know. Like when did he get croaked?"

"About 9:30 or so," says Max. "The night of the twenty-third."

You flinch. That's the same night the silver stick got lost.

Cross out a star at the Coroner.
Go to #75.

#31 *Subtract D–4 Muscle points.*

You grab this lavender bird by the collar and tell him you'll match the crease you're putting in his lapel with one you'll put in his jaw if he doesn't buzz you into the back room.

Go to #115.

#32 You hit the office door with your upper body and bust the lock.

Subtract D Muscle points.
Go to #119.

#33 No sign of Coley.

Cross out a star at the bus station and try again.
Go to #1.

#34   It's the next day. You stare out the open window and wonder whether to eat a day-old lunch, go back to the Coleys', or jump. Then in walks the brunette from Banks's Antiques, and the second show is worth the gander. Her thick black hair falls over and almost covers eyes that are hard as jet. You would bet 50 to 1 that her sweater was painted on her, and she wears slacks that aren't. "You saved my life," you say. "I almost ate this pastrami sandwich. Then I saw it was the same shade of green as your sweater." She laughs. You pour out a couple of ponies to get better acquainted.

Go to #17.

#35 *Subtract D–3 Muscle points.*
     The bum must have got sucked into his favorite sewer-hole, because he disappeared in a hurry. You shrug.

Go to #89.

#36   You finally reach the main deck with a bad case of rope burn.

Go to #102.

#37   You're looking in every dockside dive you can stand sticking your nose in. These joints smell like stale seaweed and your dirty laundry jammed together. You're looking for Vito "The Squid" Tattino, an ex-racketeer who might know something about these Skelling deals.

     Tattino lammed it out of Brooklyn eighteen years ago and ran hot cargo from the West Coast to South America. He served the Baldasaro mob as a middle-man, then he served the state five-to-ten as a fall guy. You and he are good buddies from back when his boys knocked you silly for breaking up a smuggling party he was throwing. You ask for him at one dump filled with old freight guys who work odd jobs now. Like hitting on some poor Joe who can't make a loan payment to the local shark. They all look at you with faces only a bulldog could love. You get pointed to the back room, where Tattino sits hunched over a handful of betting tickets. He's a big nothing now, running numbers instead of freight.

You use Muscle.
Go to #6.
or
You use Moxie.
Go to #105.

#38   You reach for your heater, but a bullet sings and gets stuck in your belly. It's playing taps, 'cause you're a dead man.
(You can start the case over on page 55.)

#39   *Subtract D Muscle points.*
You deck Skelling's watchdog pretty good. You'd like to do the same for your pal Ace sometime.

You slide through the kitchen and living room. In the dim hallway near the cellar door, a cat with a tiny bell around its neck leaps from the dark and meows loud like a squeaky siren. You jump only a few less yards than Jesse Owens did at the Berlin Olympics. You never figured a cigar-smoking garbage heap like Skelling would go gaga over cats. Slugs, maybe.
Go to #28.

#40   "Hey, Hart!" you yell.

Captain Hart jerks his head and tabs you being cuffed. He raises his hand and the blue boys stop squeezing you. So he remembers the time you fingered some toughs and gave *him* the headlines and handshakes. He gets you off the hook with Riker. You tip your hat on the way out. Riker points his finger at you like it was a .38 ready to spring. "Next time," he says.

Go to #1.

#41   Your car says "Goodnight, Irene" smack in the middle of evening traffic. You had a hunch this would happen when it started getting the heebie-jeebies three miles back.

Subtract 3 points from the M–M–M column of your choice.
Go to (☆) location paragraph of your choice. See map.

#42   You try Francine White's apartment again but no dice. No one answers the phone.

Go to #1.

#43   The S.S. Pizarro pitches and rolls under a full moon. Four hard guys who hold day jobs as cornerstones for the Woolworth building are flipping these crates full of silver goodies down its hold like they were playing with tiddlywinks. And you, Houdini, got ten whole minutes till 10:00 P.M. shove-off to do something about it. Duck soup. Two of the lugs drop into the ship's belly while the other two keep busy up top.

You figure you'll take them by surprise.
Go to #93.
or
You sneak yourself to one of the tie-ropes and start to shimmy across to the ship.
Go to #121.

#44   You kicked your brain into 4th and remembered that when you first met Sampson Coley he said he went to the park from 6:00 P.M. to 8:00 P.M. to read.

So now you're snooping around more trees than a mutt with a bum bladder. Benches are stacked with old fogeys out flexing their arteries. They sit and gawk at these curvy steno-pool gals who go lay in the grass, grab some descending sun, and let their skirts glide up past dimpled knees.

The crowds thin out near a sloped amphitheater, and benches dot the area. You see this thick brown limb shooting out of a tree over there. Only the brown comes from the sleeve of a cheap wool suit, and instead of leaves, it's got a Luger growing out its end. Anything what sends lead slugs at you at two hundred miles per hour is no relation to that Mother Nature dame.

You kick the heater down a hill and yank the arm from the tree. It belongs to Ace, who could double for a redwood, no sweat. He pokes your snoot with a hard right.

Go to #90.

#45   This case is chewing up your insides. You need a stiff drink and a long sleep. Right now Sally Rand could knock you over with a feather or a blown kiss.

Subtract 3 Moxie points.

Go to (☆) location paragraph of your choice. See map.

#46   *Cross out a star at Carson Docks.*

Put a star (☆) next to Francine White's apartment.

Go to #1.

#47   *Subtract D−2 Muscle points and D+3 Magnetism points.*

"I work for you," you say. "*That's* what's it to me." She tenses her muscles and snorts. Her face darkens and her lips shine with the sweat of anger. She looks gorgeous.

"You're gumming up the works, boydie-boy," she squawks. "You go cockeyed into Skelling's office with some dumb fairy tale a two-year-old wouldn't buy. Then they send me on some phony shakedown to lose me a while, but I knew it was a dupe and double-backed. Overheard what happened the other night at Coley's. What was *supposed* to happen, anyway."

Her eyes glow deadly now. Like some beautiful monster, she rises from the floor and tells *you* to sit. Like always, you listen to what a good-looking dame has to say—especially when she's pointing a .22 at your belly.

"What's that for?" you ask on the way down.

"For an eye," she says, and shoots a glance at her dresser table. You shoot one, too. Dopey move in this spot, though. She slugs you good with her gun as your head turns. But just before you drop into that final black pit, you catch her scooting out the door. You also spot a photo on the dresser. It's Zack Kelley decked out in pinstripes and cap. And hung tight to his arm and all curves in a freshly-painted sweater stands Francine White. She looks proud and plenty hungry. You're out cold.

> *Subtract D Muscle points.*
> *Cross out a star at Francine White's apartment.*
> *Put a star (☆) next to:*
>   *—Coley Antiques*
>   *—your private eye office.*
> Go to #1.

#48   You happen across Moose Mason on the street. You start to smile until you remember you sent this mug up the river five years ago for assault. He remembers too, and you and his blackjack get reacquainted.

> *Subtract 3 Muscle points.*
> Go to (☆) location paragraph of your choice. See map.

#49   *Cross out a star at Skelling Shipping Co.*
> *Put a star (☆) next to:*
>   *—Lyle Skelling's house*
>   *—Coley Antiques.*
> Go to #1.

#50   The rope is wetter than the area behind Andy Hardy's ears. Your next shimmy and grab for rope comes up empty. You fall like a stone into the ocean.

> Go to #72.

#51   You knock on Francine White's door and she opens it wide enough for an ant to walk through if it wasn't taking a deep breath at the time. "What's all this?" you ask. "I've been calling. Where you been?"

"On a wild-goose chase," she says. "What's it to you?"

You shoulder the door hard and hear a thump on the other side. The door swings open and Miss White's sitting on her sweet rump in the middle of a worn carpet.

Go to #47.

#52   You shift your peepers toward the noise. No cat this time, pal. This time it's a *gat*—with its nose pointing at you. No bell wrapped around it either. Just an itchy finger on a hair-trigger—all belonging to a two-bit flunky looking out for his boss.

He tags you across the side of your head and you drop. He drags you inside a bedroom, sits you on a wooden chair, and ties your wrists behind you to it. He makes you eat a handkerchief, too, just in case you get hungry or want to scream or something.

Subtract D Muscle points.

You kick your leg out, but he sidesteps it easy. Your blow hits a tablestand and breaks a cheap glass vase on the floor. The flunky snatches you by your soiled suit and says, "You wanna play footsy, next time I'll use the heel of my shoe instead of a hanky." Then he leaves.

You try to tip yourself back to the floor.
Go to #14.
or
You bounce yourself close to the telephone on the dresser.
Go to #88.

#53   No answer again. You slam the phone down and make for the door. The mug who eyeballed you grabs your elbow. "I just wanted ta buy you a drink for puttin' it to dat bum Vito. But maybe you tink you're too good for dock-jockeys like me." He spits and walks away. You feel like a sap.
Go to #1.

#54   You feel real good and real strong, like you could take on Jack Dempsey, your ex-wife, and Hitler—with both sets of knuckles tied behind your back.
Add 10 Muscle points.
Go to (☆) location paragraph of your choice. See map.

#55   You flip his desk drawer in the air. His gun jerks and the lead drives through the wood instead of your bones. You nearly dive through the floor, then fire two slugs into Banks's arm. He drops the heater. You step on top of him and say you want the real scoop on this Coley-Banks feud and you want it pronto.
Subtract D–2 Muscle points.

Banks cringes and says how Old Coley and he were partners years back, and when Old Coley's wife Matilda divorced the slob, she started socializing with Banks's ritzy crowd.

"You had nothing to do with it personally, I'm sure," you say.

He grunts and laughs and says, "They're both losers—father and son—with business and with women."

And what's Banks, you think. Laughing there in his own blood, with lead sitting in his arm and a mob sitting on his back. Some winner.

Cross out a star at Banks's Antiques.
Put a star (☆) next to Carson Docks.
Go to #1.

#56 You'd like to get a hold of the mug what said patience is a virtue. Ace sinks all his five available knuckles into your face, and your head twists and swims. You see about three Aces, which beats easy anything you've seen lately at the poker table. Then you black out.

Subtract D + 5 Muscle points.

After your nap, you stagger around the office until you tag Skelling's home address on a personal letter. On the way out, you see the broad at the table pop her gum and wave goodbye. It hurts when you wave back.

Go to #49.

#57   Suddenly a whole bunch of shouting tears through the ship and a shower of lead comes whipping by your head. You're a sitting duck, and the dock boys paid their quarters and want a kewpie doll real bad. You let go the rope and plunge toward the ocean. But two slugs catch your gut on the way down. So you stay down . . . you and your pal, Davy Jones . . . forever.

(You can start the case over on page 55.)

#58   A big fat blonde in feathers and pumps swoops down on you and calls you a heel, flashing her blood-red fingernails like steak knives. Seems you finked on her loverboy awhile ago on some forgery scam. You give her the glad-eye, take her by the claw, and swear you'll make it up to her.

Subtract 3 Magnetism points.

Go to (☆) location paragraph of your choice. See map.

#59   You eat lead like you were starved and fall overboard into the ocean. You sink real good.
(You can start the case over on page 55.)

#60   You hear a big commotion. Lots of people want to find you but quick. From a narrow passageway, you duck through a door that leads to the storage hold, and you nose out the ship's cargo log. You find lots of stuff what comes from Banks, but no silver stick. The stick's not taking this cruise. Neither are you, with all those hoods on board wanting your neck. You dive out the nearest porthole and into the drink. They throw bullets at you in farewell. Ain't they supposed to use flowers?
Subtract D Moxie or D Muscle points.
Go to #46.

#61   At your private eye office:
        if *no* stars are crossed out, go to #34.
        if *one* star is crossed out, go to #15.

#62   *Subtract D Moxie points.*
You don't like this target practice with your noodle as the bull's-eye.

You duck inside the main cabin of the ship.
Go to #120.
or
You decide you've had enough of this cruise and dive overboard.
Go to #72.

#63   Banks walks back in plenty steamed. He looks like someone gave him the word that his toupee came off of some dead poodle.

You tell him about Coley and the stick that got loose in the night.

Go to #5.

#64   You feel like hell. You have a three-day stubble on your face, a tongue as thick as a baloney, and bags under your eyes a bellhop wouldn't carry for less than a sawbuck.

Subtract 3 Moxie points.
Go to (☆) location paragraph of your choice. See map.

#65   Place is deader than Cleveland on a Monday night. You peep through a back window. No Banks. No lavender puffball up front. You jimmy the window open and climb in.

Subtract D + 2 Moxie points.
Go to #22.

#66   Roll the dice:
        2–4, 10 go to #114.
        5–9, 11, 12 go to #97.

#67   Louie "Creeps" Malone, an ex-con and known fence, runs up to your car and says he needs a lift to the harbor. You tell him to buzz off. He sticks a .38 in your ear so you can hear better. You tell him to hop in and make himself cozy.

Subtract 3 points from the M–M–M column of your choice, worrying about the time slipping from your mitts.
Go to (☆) location paragraph of your choice. See map.

#68   *Subtract D Moxie points.*

You feed this filly a line about being a lawyer, a government agent, an ex-prizefighter, a part-time movie producer, until her pretty noodle swims long enough to drown in your palaver.

"Oh," she says, like it registered somewhere behind the peroxide. "Yeah, I think I heard of youse." She nods. Funny—*youse* never heard of youse. She lets you see Skelling just 'cause you're that big a shot.

Go to #73.

#69   You're wearing your heels out circling the shop like it was a fat light bulb and you some screwy moth. You're worn out.

Subtract D–3 Muscle points.
Go to #95.

#70   You feel like a regular wiseguy lately, cracking off to anyone in earshot. You're backchatting to cabbies, hotel clerks; you're even calling your landlady "sister."

Add 10 points to the M–M–M column of your choice.
Go to (☆) location paragraph of your choice. See map.

#71   You work your metal pick and make nice with the lock till it falls open like a fresh hot bun at Cora's Diner. You wish Cora did likewise.

Subtract D Moxie points.
Go to #119.

#72   *Subtract D–2 Muscle points.*

You tread water and wave the S.S. Pizarro goodbye as it steams off and its horn bellows something like "So long, sucker" in E flat. Oh, yeah, you wave that stolen silver stick goodbye, too. Next stop—Mexico.

Go to #46.

#73   Lyle Skelling, the company prez, is fat, bald, smokes cigars, and stares at your belly like he envies it and wants a trade. You say you're a friend of Zack Kelley's from the Army and can't seem to find him. Skelling rolls his stogey from the left side of his mouth to the right. You say you got some dough marked for Kelley that you owe him. Skelling rolls his stogey from the right side of his mouth to the left.

You figure if anybody's got personality, this guy is lousy with it.

Skelling's eyes look up. "Ace here's the only friend he got, pal," he says with a snort.

You look up. Way up. Ace is tall. Ace might have to bend at the waist to smooch the Statue of Liberty. Like Tommy Dorsey, you figure Ace looks "in the mood"—in the mood to bend some of your bones.

You think you'll beat him to the sap and you kick your oxfords at his gut.

Go to #26.

or

You figure Ace was called in to be brass-knuckle window-dressing so that Skelling can tell you the score, like who's boss around there. You wait and see what comes out of Skelling's fat mouth besides cigar juice.

Go to #56.

#74   Your car says "Sayonara, Charlie" smack in the middle of noon traffic. You had a hunch this would happen when the piston heads started playing taps under the hood three miles back.

Subtract 3 points from the M—M—M column of your choice.
Go to (☆) location paragraph of your choice. See map.

#75   It was a cinch sneaking in to see Max, but not so easy sneaking out. The cops at the main desk must have woken up from their beauty sleep, and they can smell a shamus on the premises.

"Look who's here," says one flatfoot.

You don't even give his mug the time of day. You keep walking. Then you walk into a brick wall what's got a name—Lt. Riker.

"Look who's here," he says.

"And they say the force doesn't have any independent thinkers," you say. "You boys have to stop keeping each other company so much. Expand your vocabulary a little. Four-word sentences even."

"We gotta talk," Riker sneers, and grabs your arm.

"See what I mean?" you crack. He and the other badges head you to the interrogation room. You think you see Capt. Hart. He maybe could get you out of this spot.

Go to #11.

#76   The street shakes with the palsy of jerking cars going nowhere. Yet Coley's shop sits there and plays dead, real still and numb, like the top of your skull. Francine White socked plenty hard for a broad having so many soft parts on her. A sign that says "Closed for Dinner" covers half the glass door. You peep inside. The kid, Ansel, is propped on a broom. His face is blank, his body motionless. He turns and looks at you. His eyes are round and vacant. They're like two Grand Canyons, only deeper. He turns away. A reflection in the glass shows movement behind you. A blur shuffles and coughs, stops, then makes tracks fast. It's the bum what tumbled onto the stiff. You race after him.

Go to #83.

#77   *Subtract D Moxie points.*
You tell him you're going to nose out what closet he came out of and who's on the hanger next to him if he doesn't buzz you into the back room.

Go to #115.

#78   The shipping office is dark and empty. Just like you wanted it.

You use Muscle.
Go to #32.
or
You use Moxie.
Go to #71.

#79   Two coppers on patrol are tailing you so close they might as well sit in your trunk. You try to shake them.

Roll the dice:

> 2–3   You bust onto one of those ugly new freeways and get the law dizzy in a concrete pretzel they call a cloverleaf. *Add 5 points to the M–M–M column of your choice.* Go to (☆) location paragraph of your choice. See map.
>
> 4–6   You dodge into Fast Sammy's used car joint. The cops can't spot your junkheap in with all the other junkheaps. Go to (☆) location paragraph of your choice. See map.
>
> 7–10 Can't shake them. *Subtract 2 points from the M–M–M column of your choice.* (Throw dice again.)
>
> 11–12 Can't shake them. *Subtract 5 points from the M–M–M column of your choice.* (Throw dice again.)

#80   It isn't Hart. What it is is a long afternoon on the hot seat with Riker.

Go to #94.

#81   The door opens nice and easy. A gray blur leaps toward you. You jump only a few less yards than Jesse Owens did at the Berlin Olympics. It's a cat with a tiny bell dangling from its collar. You're tempted to strangle the furry runt for almost sending you down the cellar stairs airmail, but you always had a soft spot for animals. Except for the kind that pack rods and work for Skelling.

Go to #28.

#82   You look real spiffy. Your pants have only a few less wrinkles than those leatherskin cronies who read dime novels at the beach, and your trenchcoat looks like you slept in it for a month. It's only been a week and a half.

Subtract 3 Magnetism points.
Go to (☆) location paragraph of your choice. See map.

#83   Roll the dice:
      2–6 go to #103.
      7–12 go to #107.

#84 🔫 NOW—if you have *minus* (–) Muscle points: Go to #57.
      if you have *plus* (+) Muscle points: Go to #36.

#85   You fall into the tree and get splinters along your back as you slide down. Ace snatches you by the neck. His hand makes like a wrench and starts twisting your Adam's apple so it can stick itself out the back of your neck. Your fists thump on that granite arm of his, but no dice. You fall limp in his mitt. Your face turns pale white. Your heart packed up and quit on you. You're dead, pally.

      (You can start the case over on page 55.)

#86   The Coroner is Max Yablanski. He's seen more naked bodies than Howard Hughes. Only Hughes gets them hot, and Max gets them cold. Max is on lunchbreak, gnawing his usual tomatoes on toast. When you've touched as much dead meat as Max, it's hard swallowing a baloney sandwich. You give him the usual song and dance, and his eyes look tired and red. He knows he owes you one.

Go to #30.

#87 Some mug is tailing you. He's your average-looking hard guy, not quite as tall as the Chrysler building. You feel frisky and confront him. He bounces a blackjack off your head.

Subtract 3 Muscle points.

Go to (☆) location paragraph of your choice. See map.

#88 *Subtract D Moxie points.*

So you got yourself next to a telephone. Now what? You need your mouth, and there's a nose rag stuffed in it. You're not thinking real good. You try to tip yourself on the floor near that broken glass.

Go to #14.

#89 You know where he lives. Under your bedroom window. Rattling garbage cans—6:00 A.M. sharp.

Objectives #4 and #5: Who killed the man in the trash bin? Why?

Cross out a star at Coley Antiques.

Put a star (☆) next to:

—the Coroner

—the Ex-Racketeer (who might know about Skelling).

You call the law about the stiff in the garbage.

Go to #1.

#90   *Subtract D + 3 Muscle points.*
NOW—if you still have *plus* (+) Muscle *and plus* (+)
Magnetism points: go to #122.
if you have *minus* (–) Muscle *or minus* (–) Magnetism points:
Roll the dice:
2–4 go to #85.
5–12 go to #122.

#91   Your car says "Adios, muchachos" smack in the
middle of morning traffic. You had a hunch this
would happen when the engine started doing the
rumba three miles back.
Subtract 3 points from the M–M–M column of your choice.
Go to (☆) location paragraph of your choice. See map.

#92   They drag you out and start slapping you around.
You sock one of the cops hard on the chin. He folds in
a neat pile on the curb. The other one lays off. You're
going downtown all right, but without the rough
stuff.
Cross out a star at Banks's Antiques.
Go to #94.

#93   *Subtract D + 3 Muscle points.*
You make like Errol Flynn and swing on board
with your mitts around a cable hook and your feet
sunk into one mug's belly. He shrieks as he flips over
and hits the drink. The other lug whirls, holding a
crate in his arms, and uses up half his vocabulary by
saying, "Huh?" You catch the back of his knee with
your shoe. He buckles and the crate lands on his fingers and you knock him cold. You sneak up the
gangplank and hit the main deck.
Go to #102.

#94   In the interrogation room they grill you good. They keep calling you "pally" and siccing some lug with long nasal hairs on you. Give these badges credit. They play rough and know where it hurts.

Subtract one die roll from your weakest M–M–M column.

They got nothing to hold you on except maybe three counts of exposing facial stubble on public property. They toss you out on the seat of your trench.

Go to #1.

#95   No sign of Coley. Lots of cops, though. Banks must have given the law a permanent post outside his door, 'cause two prowl cars sandwich your car in real tight like you were the white stuff in an Oreo cookie.

Two badges get out of the car and recognize you right away. That's why they don't bother opening your door. They'd rather pull you through the window.

Roll the dice:
    2–8 go to #92.
    9–12 go to #125.

#96 You stop in at a local joint and buy a bottle of good hooch to give you that extra pep. Besides, you couldn't think of anything else for dinner.
Add 10 points to the M–M–M column of your choice.
Go to (☆) location paragraph of your choice. See map.

#97 You slip out clean of coppers.
Go to #1.

#98 When you wake up, you see a blurry dollface rubbing your temples real soft. It's the peroxide babe of a secretary, wearing a ruby-lipped pout on her kisser. She feels sorry for you, but not half as much as you do.

She wonders how you fell. "Hard," you say. You notice that Skelling and the Cardiff giant took a powder somewhere. The frail wiggles off to get some more cold water for your lump. You prefer Scotch, straight up. You rifle her desk and find Skelling's home address. You figure a social call may be just the ticket someday.
Go to #49.

#99 You run into ex–Detective Sergeant Murphy, a crooked cop from way back, who's pounding a beat now instead of serving time like he oughtta. You crack wise about his feet getting flatter, so he saps you for the exercise.
Subtract 3 Muscle points.
Go to (☆) location paragraph of your choice. See map.

#100   You brush the chicken bones and leftover canned tuna off your trench and climb a wooden fence. You see your bum huffing and puffing a garbage dump away. You're on his case again.
Go to #107.

#101   Roll the dice:
            2–7 go to #81.
            8–12 go to #106.

#102   You check the tags on some of the cargo. No sign of Banks's name. Suddenly you hear a shout from a higher deck. You see a shadow on the bridge and the twinkle of moonlight off an automatic. Probably the captain, you figure. His bullets buzz by your ear like hungry flies at a fruit stand.

            You jump inside the main cabin of the ship.
            Go to #60.
            or
            You run to the opposite deck.
            Go to #110.

#103   The bum turns a corner up ahead. You play leap-frog with a trashcan and the can wins. The bum is getting away . . . again.
            Subtract D–3 Muscle or D–2 Moxie points.
            Go to #100.

#104   *Subtract D + 2 Moxie points.*
            The cellar is plenty dark. You grope around until you spot a thin line of light shooting around a door-frame up a flight of stairs. You climb to the top and

park your ear on the lumber. You hear the tinkle from some little bell.

You try to open the door real slow.
Go to #101.
or
You don't like surprises. You go back out the cellar window and play pattycake with the gunsel out back.
Go to #39.

#105   *Subtract D Moxie points.*
You threaten to squeal about his bookie racket to Lt. Riker and the bunko squad unless he spills some beans.
Go to #8.

#106   The door is locked. Swell. You have to bump your way through the ink-black cellar and out the window. You have to put the slug to the gunsel at the front door just the same.
Go to #39.

#107   The bum thinks he's shaken your tail and flops under a ratty blanket he's doubled over a clothesline as a tent. You tear the woolly wall from its ropes.
"Sorry, bub," you say. "This Campfire Girls meeting is a bust." The bum snatches a heavy metal object from his bag and takes a swing at you. You stiff-arm the ragheap and he stays down, breathing hard. "I didn't do nothin'," he screams. "Nothin'." You can't even flap your lips in response. You stand stopped in your tracks like you just saw the bogeyman. That metal hunk the bum tried to part your hair

with is no ordinary sap. It's silver and tall and worth eight thousand beans. "Where'd you snatch the stick, pally?" you snap.

"From the trash bin," he says, "just before I seen the stiff. Honest. I stashed it in my coat before you butted your nose in."

You give the silver stick the once-over. The white satin base got itself a deep, deep red from bloodstains you couldn't get out with an eviction notice. Your brain flashes and your watch says 6:30 P.M. You better root out Young Coley quick.

Cross out a star at Coley Antiques.
IMPORTANT: you MUST go to #127 (Skelling's house) now if you haven't gone there before. Then and only then:
Put a star (☆) next to:
  –Banks's Antiques
  –the bus station
  –the park.
(But there is only *one* correct choice out of the three, based on the clues revealed in this case; the other ones lead nowhere and cost M–M–M points. Choose wisely. Once you get to the correct location, you should not go on to either of the other two.)
Go to #1.

#108   *Subtract D + 2 Magnetism points.*

She laughs at your wisecrack and swishes in her seat. Her nylons purr. You give her that cheap smile of yours and ask to see the boss, Skelling. In a flash, she points you to his office door. Then she points her pretty finger at you and snaps her gum like she shot off a .45. She gives you a big wink as you enter Skelling's office.

Go to #73.

#109   *Subtract D Muscle points.*

Your shoe sinks deep into Ace's belly. He collapses like a punctured sack of flour. You stand over Skelling, who stares at you with his eyes on fire.

"I don't like big apes breathin' on my lapels," you say. "Curls 'em up." You walk out the door.

Outside, the secretary gives you another once-over. You do the same, only your hand pockets some of Skelling's personal files. In the car, you dig up Skelling's home address among the papers. You might play post office sometime.

Go to #49.

#110   No protection there either. The shadow on the bridge follows you easy and lets fly a few more slugs your way.

NOW—if you still have *plus* (+) Muscle points: Go to #62.
   if you have *minus* (−) Muscle points:
      Roll the dice:
         2–9 go to #62.
         10–12 go to #59.

#111   The lug shows his chipped-tooth smile and shakes your mitt. "I loves seein' Vito eat it. He done me dirty years ago." He buys you a drink. You feel like his boyhood hero or something.
     Add 10 M–M–M points to the column of your choice.
     Go to #42.

#112   Soon as your paw hits paper, a big hand squeezes your upper arm like a tube of Pepsodent. "What are you doing?" its owner says.
     Subtract D Moxie points.
     You come clean as to why you came, and hope that his finger-vise eases up enough so your blood can stop taking a detour at your elbow. Some grip for a guy decked out in a shirt your maiden aunt would use for kitchen curtains.
     "Coley, you say?" Banks lets go your arm and slams shut the drawer with his knee. His face winces at the name. Your hand is glad to see your arteries open for business again.
     Go to #5.

#113   Outside of town, you enter a small, shabby, wooden box of a building. There's a leaky sink in one corner and a card table in the other with a secretary snapping gum behind it. If it didn't say Skelling Shipping Co. on the door, you would've laid odds it was the john at the Y.M.C.A.
     You bat your baby browns at the table girl and ask, "Where's the old man who hands you wash towels for two bits?"
     Her eyes are bright and her head is empty. "You don't mean Mr. Skelling, do you?" she asks.
     "Close enough," you crack.

You use Moxie.
Go to #68.
or
You use Magnetism.
Go to #108.

#114   The long arm of the law in the person of Patrol-
man O'Malley collars you at the back door. He says,
"Lieutenant Riker is feeling restless and needs a good
workout." But for you, that means a workover.
O'Malley takes you downtown.
Go to #94.

#115   You get buzzed, natch. The flunky yaps at Banks,
all flustered like a goose with a hotfoot. "That's all
right, Eugene," says Banks. Eugene leaves in a sulk.
You figure this Banks comes right out of the same can
as Eugene, only older, harder, and more sure in the
clutch. He wears clothes well and all his pieces fit in
place, including the one made of hair sitting on top of
his noodle. Only things that don't tumble are big,
strong hands. The kind made to squeeze too hard.
You pass Banks your card. The brunette gets a gander
at it, but Banks flashes a mean eye at her and escorts
her out of the shop. You notice she left what look like
shipment papers for him. You also notice a shiny little
Luger sleeping in his bottom drawer with some pink
stationery.

You reach your mitts into the drawer to get a better gander at the papers.
Go to #112.
or

You peep out the window to see what Banks and the dame are doing.

Go to #2.

or

You stand and stare at some hatchet-faced wooden Indian what reminds you of your ex-wife's emotional range, and wait for Banks.

Go to #63.

#116 The noise is a flunky for Skelling spotting you from another room. He shouts and you fly out a back window, which is no big deal. If you get to leave a joint, *any* joint, by using the door fifty percent of the time, you feel lucky.

Go to #18.

#117 You blow through red lights plenty fast, hoping the coppers are eyeing sidewalk nylons or taking siestas, two of the three things they're real good at. The other is breaking your chops whenever possible.

Go to (☆) location paragraph of your choice. See map.

#118 Some dumb gunsel has been following you for blocks, probably holding a gat and a grudge. You try to shake him fast.

Roll the dice:

2–3 Can't shake him. *Subtract 5 points from the M–M–M column of your choice.* (Throw dice again.)

4–7 Can't shake him. *Subtract 2 points from the M–M–M column of your choice.* (Throw dice again.)

8–10 You duck into Wang Lee's laundry and hide behind the dirty towels. The gunsel loses you. You throw a few yen to Wang for the consideration. Go to (☆) location paragraph of your choice. See map.

11–12 You turn on the gunsel in an alley and flatten his nose for him. *Add 5 points to the M–M–M column of your choice.* Go to (☆) location paragraph of your choice. See map.

#119   You case the file cabinets and thumb a stock of shipping orders and receipts like the one Francine White slipped to Banks. Most look like they mean business—shipments of gold items, some silver, lots of jewelry and antiques. You hit one shipment order for antique goods *not* delivered to Skelling by Sampson Coley. In fact, some Coley scrawls cover the paper with words like NEVER! and DROP DEAD!! and others Amy Vanderbilt says don't go with hors d'oeuvres.

Cross out a star at Skelling Shipping Co.

A red light flashes around the room. You see it's from a car parked right outside packed with coppers. You figure Skelling must have tipped them off. He sure has a big payroll list.

Go to #66.

#120   You bump into the first mate and he bops you one with his compass. You see stars you can't navigate too good with.

Subtract D–2 Muscle points.

You literally deck him with a good right hand. You're not waiting for the second mate and the rest of this crooked navy.

You dive overboard.

Go to #72.

#121   Subtract D Moxie points.

The ropes are real wet and real cold. And real slippery. You feel like one of those metal monkey toys what go up and down a stick and get broken in a half an hour. You hope one of those loading boys doesn't spot your tightrope act, 'cause you break easy, too.

Roll the dice:
> 2–3 go to #84.
> 4–9 go to #36.
> 10–12 go to #50.

#122   You almost take the count. But you got enough gray matter left cooking to flash your .38 and plug two nickel-sized holes through Ace's ribs. He sways a bit like he's confused and thinking about falling but he's not sure. You convince him with another piece of lead. The three holes you made in his body are enough to keep him down for good. You notice a smaller-caliber hole that runs through his coat sleeve.

Ace's target, otherwise known as Sampson Coley, runs over from the bench he was reading on and looks surprised. Suddenly he sees Ace and starts to laugh.

"What's the gag?" you ask.

He looks at you and says, "He's dead."

"Oh," you say. "Yeah—I got a million of them."

You jam your rod back into your holster.

Go to #1.

#123   The bus station is a wall-to-wall nut factory. Buses to Vegas line one side, choked by old dames with stiff blonde wigs and winged sunglasses and their spouses who have obviously cornered the market on plaid pants. The other side of the depot holds a handful of local buses loading up the after-work crowd.

You figure you need a scam and need one fast. You run from bus to bus and make like an inspector late for dinner and on a fast passenger check. What you don't tell them is that it's only one passenger you're trying to nose out—Sampson Coley.

Subtract D–2 Moxie points.
Go to #33.

#124   Roll the dice:
2–5, 11 go to #116.
6–10, 12 go to #52.

#125   Before they can get their mitts on you, you put the Buick in reverse and slam the cop car behind you real hard, sending it back ten feet into a nice picket fence. You screech into forward with two flatfoots shaking their paws at you in your rearview mirror.

Cross out a star at Banks's Antiques and try again.
Go to #1.

#126   *Subtract D Magnetism points.*

Miss Watson tells you Ansel Coley is a real disturbed and inhibited sort of kid what gets upset easy. And his father is always being a pill making goo-goo eyes at her all the time when he drops his son off. "What about the mother?" you ask. She says that she had a rep for being a tramp, a run-around. She supposedly went to the shop once to show off her current

live-in gent to Young Coley and to gloat. Ansel
snapped at the sight of the new Joe and threw a fit on
the spot. You ask if Ansel maybe would pinch things.
Miss Watson tell you nix, 'cause he doesn't understand
the value of objects.

"Ansel's father, Sampson, understands, though,"
she says. "Even though Old Coley has the reputation
of being the most influential antique dealer on the
West Coast, Sampson is always bragging to me about
how *he* controls the bankroll at the shop, how his old
father is just a nuisance and would be better off
dead."

"Real heart o' gold beating in that guy," you say.
"If it were," she smiles, "he'd have gotten an estimate
and hocked it long ago." You laugh. You look at
Amy Watson like you'd like to get a house and some
babies with her. She glows softly at you. Then you
tip your hat and blow through the door into the dusty
snarl of people and ambitions.

Cross out a star at Greely's Special School.
Go to #1.

#127 Skelling's live-in joint sure ain't no Y.M.C.A.
washroom. It's real plush and bigger than his belly,
and that says a lot. You figure he's in the gravy but
not from exporting bottle-caps.

You climb down a cellar window.
Go to #104.
or
You punch out a drowsy gunsel guarding the back
door.
Go to #39.

Hard-Boiled Points (Case B) (150 points)

Objectives #1 and #2: Ansel Coley "took"
the candlestick-holder from the shop (in fact,
he threw it away with Kelley's body)   __10__ points
   . . . because he was afraid his father
would find it ruined by the bloodstains and
be angry and beat him (as he did when he
found the broken cup).   __15__ points

Objective #3: Zack Kelley is dead, found in
the trash bin by the scavenging bum.   __5__ points

Objectives #4 and #5: Ansel Coley *actually*
killed Zack Kelley . . .   __40__ points
   . . . because Kelley was his mother's
lover, and he went berserk seeing him, just as
he did the last time; *and/or* Kelley was there
to kill Sampson and Ansel saved him.   __25__ points

Objectives #6 and #7: Ace *actually* killed
Francine White Coley . . .   __30__ points
   . . . because she tried to kill Skelling
and/or Ace as revenge for their getting Zack
Kelley killed in their failed bump-off of
Sampson Coley.   __25__ points

Hard-Boiled Rating (Case B)

105–150 points . . . . One Tough Egg
 80–100 points . . . . Gumshoe with Guts
 50–80 points . . . . Soft-Boiled Shamus
 0–45 points . . . . Near-Sighted Peeper

The Final Dope (Case B)

You're sprawled out on a wooden seat outside courtroom 17. Your hat slants over your eyes. A court cop bops you on the noggin with his stick.

"What do you think you're doin'?" he says.

"I call it resting," you say. "Sometimes I call it rest for short. Sometimes I just call it Bruce."

His face looks troubled. In police hierarchy, court cops fall somewhere just below the flatfoot on the beat and just above motorcycle helmets.

Suddenly the courtroom doors swing wide and the joint's hopping. Coppers lead Ansel Coley to the cellrooms through popping flashbulbs. The daily rags tout the kid as some dragon-killer who croaked a gangland pro. You laugh. Zack Kelley was some washed-up gorilla who went from pro wrestler to punk hitman, that's all. Lyle Skelling was his boss and Ace was his trainer.

Your blackboard angel, Miss Amy Watson, staggers outside. She stops, gazes up at you, then falls into your arms, crying. She says, "Ansel is being sent to the state institution for tests. He'll probably spend the rest of his life there." She blows her pretty tooter with a hanky she pulls from her purse. Lucky she didn't ask you for yours. Last time you used it was to check the oil on your junkheap.

"Well," you say, "the squirt sure screwed up the hit on his old man. Give him that. Skelling had Sampson on the phone for an hour waiting to hear the kill. He didn't figure that when Kelley snuck in, the kid would go berserk when he recognized his mother's loverboy again. Then again, maybe—" You stop.

She says, "I know what you're going to say. Maybe he just did it to protect his father. 'Cause he loved him in some way because he *was* his father. That's what you were going to say."

"Yeah, maybe," you say. "That'd be a hard one to peddle to Ripley's, though, wouldn't it?" She nods and squeezes you close. Sampson Coley slumps out of the courtroom and chews on a cigarette like it was gum. "A *real* hard one," you mumble. Coley flashes green eyes at you, wrapped around this dreamboat in pumps.

He says, "Guess you couldn't do jack to save this kid. You and your school. You and your tough-guy talk and gumshoe routine. Before, I had me a vegetable. Now—now I got a public humiliation. Like a goddamn freak show, I gotta be showing my prize attraction! Thanks a million."

Amy turns away with her head down.

You tense and sock Coley hard on the nose. He flies back and down and hits the marble floor out cold.

You feel better. But not much.

Amy grabs your hand and slowly leads you down the hallway and outside. Her complexion shines bright and clear through the downtown haze.

THE END
(Case B)
"THE HOT STICK"

Case C

Money Never Bleeds

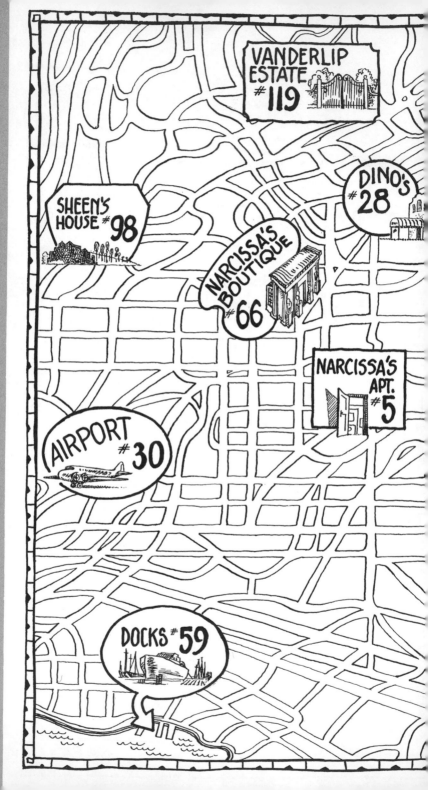

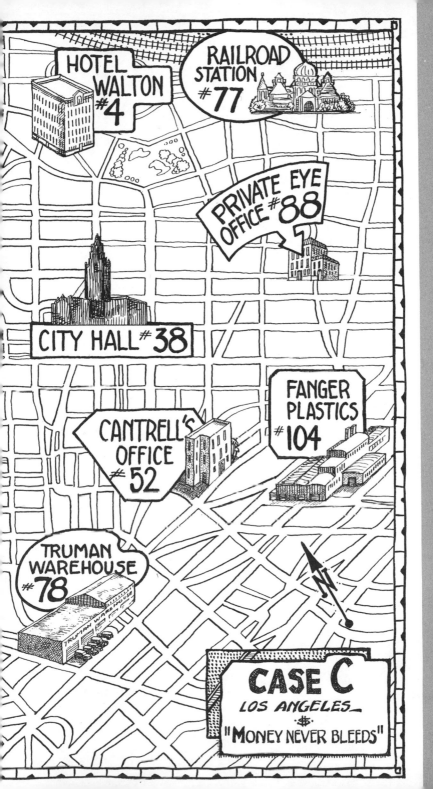

Objectives: 7

Difficulty:

M–M–M points: 145

Money Never Bleeds

It's Friday morning. You're having your breakfast bottle of Scotch—over easy, hold the toast—when a uniformed silhouette hits the frosty glass on your door. You're about to say something endearing like, "Buzz off, flatfoot," but a chauffeur enters instead. He says his name is Norris Blakely. He's an old guy, but he's hard, and the sculptured silver hair under his cap makes him look polished and fit. He says a Mrs. Norma Vanderlip would like to see you downstairs in her limo. "Oh, yeah," you say, "I saw some big black meat-wagon pull up here from the window. I figured someone thought I was stiffed." What you really figure is that this Vanderlip dame must think your office is just a front for the town dump. All because you got a three-inch layer of butts instead of a carpet, and curtains made of last week's racing sheet.

You hop in the back of this house on wheels and meet a high society dame in her late fifties who's got so many diamonds hanging off her she looks like a chandelier. You've seen her puss in the dailies. Only when the society columns are next to the sports page, natch. She was just widowed from her second husband, so now she owns a few companies and a lotta millions. She starts yapping a mile a minute about how her only child, her precious Narcissa, is running around with hoodlums, and her boyfriend is part of some awful gang of gamblers. You're not sure whether she's rattled about her precious daughter or her own precious reputation among the stuffed shirts. She hands you a picture of

Narcissa and tells you to keep an eye on her. It'd be hard not to—tall, twenty-one, blond hair that waves at you like summer trees, and a nose shooting up in the air like her mother's. You get the lowdown—where she lives, where she runs a boutique, when she hangs out at the Mermaid Club.

"Report back as soon as you know anything to the Vanderlip Estate," she says. "And don't talk to her, for Heaven's sake, just look, and from a goodly distance."

"Hold your water, lady," you say. "I had my shots." And you slam the door behind you.

Objective #1: Who is Narcissa's boyfriend?
You head up to the Mermaid Club to nose around and maybe get a line on Narcissa's best boy. You hit the jackpot. She's on the dance floor and stuck like flypaper to this crew-cut gent in a monkey-suit. She's wearing a pink silk dress and looks like a million. She'll be worth as much one day. Even more. When the music stops, the crew-cut leads Narcissa to their corner table, then goes over to two ugly bruisers—one's a real shrimp dressed in baby blue from top to toe, the other one's wide and has a building brick for a nose. Suddenly, Narcissa gets up and runs to a Joe who just entered, and they squeeze each other on the sly. The Joe is greasy, with big worried eyes. He smokes a dark cigarette and is full of nerves. Little Boy Blue and Brick-Nose walk over quick, put their meat-hooks on them and yank them into a back room. Little Boy Blue is having an extra swell time squeezing the blonde as hard as he can. The crew-cut starts beefing real loud and runs into the back too. You're about to join the party when the pulse of a gun shakes the joint. All the dames start screaming and the guys start grabbing their drinks and running. You find Little Boy Blue in the back room pumped in the head with a .22. Everyone else lammed out of there. Your intuition and a prowl-car siren tell you to do the same.

Objectives #2 and #3: Who killed Little Boy Blue? Why?
Put a star (☆) *next to:*
    —Narcissa's apartment
    —Narcissa's Boutique
    —the Vanderlip Estate.
(Map for Case C on page 106–107.)
Go to #1.

#1   Rubbing elbows with this Vanderlip bunch makes you feel dirty inside. Money kind of does that to you. Except when it can buy you a full bottle and new bottoms for your wing tips.

      Speaking of which, your shoes are getting so worn you can feel your socks scraping the sidewalks. That's what this job does to you. The streets are tough on a man's sole.

      You hate yourself for that one.

      Throw the dice *1 die at a time* **and refer to the chart below to see which paragraph # you must go to.**

Street Chart

		1st die throw					
		1	2	3	4	5	6
	1	117	45	41	7	48	117
	2	23	117	96	82	74	10
2nd die throw	3	13	54	117	117	19	96
	4	96	118	117	117	70	79
	5	67	91	64	99	117	87
	6	117	96	29	58	96	117

#2   Brick-Nose's belly must've got better. He barely
flinches, and smacks you with his gun hand. He grabs
you before you fall and puts the squeeze on your
throat. Big red spots doing the shimmy blind your
eyes and are the last things you get to see.
(You may start the case over on page 109.)

#3   Across from the Hotel Walton stands "Ponies"
McGee, hawking the daily rag at five cents a pop. His
real dough comes from being a one-man floating
bookie joint. The bottom paper is always turned to tomorrow's race sheet for a fast peek when a customer
needs a tip and quick odds. He gives you the eye.

You walk over to him to see what he knows.
Go to #123.
or
You can't remember if you ever covered the rest
of the bet you made on that glue-factory filly in the
seventh at Pimlico last week. So you make like he's as
visible as air and go inside the Walton.
Go to #50.

#4   At the Hotel Walton:
          if *no* stars are crossed out, go to #121.
          if *one* star is crossed out, go to #3.

#5   At Narcissa's apartment:
          if *no* stars are crossed out, go to #97.
          if *one* star is crossed out, go to #129.

#6   If you were one of the slab-boys at the morgue,
          you would pronounce this joint D.O.A. Now you
          know why the goon out front is feeling for iron—if
          you shot one off in here, you might wake these stiffs
          up. You grap the casino's cigarette girl.
              Subtract D Magnetism points.
              "No shakedown, honey," you say. "I need some
          dope."
              She points to a drunk giving her the eye and says,
          "How about him?"
              A sawbuck puts a lid on her wising off, and she
          spills some facts. The dump's owned by a Dawson
          Sheen, and it's going under for a third time. Sheen
          needs bucks fast or else the mob takes over. Then she's
          looking for a new job. You ask where he lives and she
          tells you. You ask where *she* lives and she throws a
          drink on your lap. A sawbuck just doesn't go as far as
          it used to.
              Cross out a star at Truman Warehouse.
              Put a star (☆) next to Sheen's house.
              Go to #1.

#7   Your office rent is two months behind, and your
          landlady is down the block looking for someone to sap
          with her broomstick—preferably you. You duck into
          the nearest gin joint until she passes.
              Gain 10 Moxie points from downing a few ponies.
              Go to (☆) location paragraph of your choice. See map.

#8   You walk up this long brick driveway. On the way, you see some Mex in grubby dungarees outside the gardening shed. You keep walking up the driveway. And walking. You figure if this goes on much longer you'll be in Oz by sundown. But before you can say "Where's Toto?" a big mutt the size of Kansas comes barking and yapping and running and heading for your neck.

> You run like hell to get back to your car.
> **Go to #73.**
> *or*
> You run like hell for the garden shed.
> **Go to #81.**

#9   Norris is working a rag on the limo so hard that if he was ever able to smile, his dentures would gleam off the hood. You slip by him in the driveway.
> *Subtract D–2 Moxie points.*
> **Go to #12.**

#10   Traffic is as congested as a three-pack-a-day Camel smoker in a steambath.
> *Subtract 3 points from the M–M–M column of your choice.*
> **Go to (☆) location paragraph of your choice. See map.**

#11   On the way up the stairwell you shoot a look out the window. You think you see the Vanderlip limo sitting across the street, and now that you think about it, it was there when you came. Carl's apartment door is half open. A bellhop is delivering Scotch and Carl is on the phone swigging. Colored bottles line his dresser, and they're not filled with M & M's.

He says, "Right . . . ten-thirty . . . Sure . . . I'm taking a sleeper." He pops a pill and tells the bellhop to scram. No tip means he's hard-up and sweating. As the hop leaves, you see Carl stick a .22 in his belt. "I'm being followed," he whispers into the phone. "Yeah, still . . . I'm *not* panicking!"

The door closes. Suddenly, who should join your peepshow but your old buddy, Brick-Nose, pointing a Luger at your bellybutton.

"Lay off the Vanderlip kid," he says.

"I can't help it," you say. "I have an itch for blondes that I love to scratch."

"The hell with her," he interrupts. "Just lay off, on account of we need the dough quick."

You swing for his noggin.
Go to #42.
or
You kick at his stomach.
Go to #112.
or
You body-roll into his legs.
Go to #33.
or
You shrug and nod like you mean it.
Go to #86.

#12 The front door is locked tight. You'd like to make a surprise entrance. You spot two open windows.

You climb through the window to the game room.
Go to #111.
or
You climb through the window to the study.
Go to #63.

#13   Traffic is almost as heavy as John D. Rockefeller's money belt.
Subtract 3 points from the M–M–M column of your choice.
Go to (☆) location paragraph of your choice. See map.

#14   Nice work. You get yourself into his office unannounced. Cantrell is jawing on the phone and doesn't see you. You recognize him as the crew-cut at the club with the monkey-suit. A couple of client files cover his desk—Jackson Associates, Truman Warehouse, Langhorn Electricians' Union. He finally sees you, slams the phone down, and starts squawking at you. When you ask him about the Vanderlips, he snarls about how the Mrs. is dirt, how she likes her nose clean and hates her children. You're too busy noticing his face become a beet and don't see him going for his bottom drawer. Sure enough, a .38 shows its nose at you. "Get out," he says. "I've said too much." As you back out, smiling, you spot a framed photo of Narcissa sitting on his desk.
Cross out a star at Cantrell's Office.
Go to #1.

#15   You move toward the fire escape but Riker uses either his shoulder or his head to bust in your door. He's got his rod out, natch, like you're wanted by the F.B.I. for too many mustard stains on your tie.

"Where you going, shamus?" he asks.

"I was just going to see you about this screwy case I'm wrapped up in," you say.

"Same here," he says. "But you always use the window to leave this dump?"

"Docs say I got a fear of swinging objects. Glass doors. Coppers' billy clubs. You know."

Riker waves in two badges with their sticks raised. "Like these?" he says.

"Those are them," you say, and dive out the window and into the arms of another flatfoot. He smiles.

"You're going downtown," says Riker. The guy's got a gift for the obvious.

Go to #94.

#16   The records don't show any Carl Reagan ever working for Fanger Plastics.

Cross out a star at **Fanger Plastics.**
Go to #1.

#17   *Subtract D + 1 Magnetism points.*

They all giggle like a chorus of angels. Except one. She's the prune at the third desk with the pencil growing out of her skull. You figure she sticks it there to plug the leak. "Mrs. Wilma Humpty," says her nameplate. A pert redhead puckers her puss to get the biddy's goat and then leads you to Cantrell's door.

Go to #14.

#18   You don't breathe, either.

(You can start the case over on page 109.)

#19   Your ex-wife grabs you on the street. You swear she's looking more and more like Mussolini every day. She sings the alimony blues while you dig down hard for all the charm you can muster to get away.

Subtract 3 Moxie points.

Go to (☆) location paragraph of your choice. See map.

#20   You're raising your hand to try some other angle when her body starts to tremble.

"He okay?" she says. "You do something to him? He all right?" She cocks the hammer on the shotgun.

Her panic makes you bolt down the driveway and dive toward the shrubs. She lets go a blast that catches you flush in the side. You land in a heap on top of the azalea bush. You're only good for fertilizer now.

(You can start the case over on page 109.)

#21   "Nothing," you say, and you backpedal an eighth of an inch at a time so as Volner shouldn't notice. You should be out of the store in six weeks at that rate. You tip your hat to moon-eyed Judy, avoid Dan Volner's forearms, and blow. You figure Volner could dead-lift you one-handed. It's the *dead* part that keeps your dogs pedalling down the pavement.

Go to #116.

#22   You blow out the side alley as the cops screech to a halt and chase you on their little flat feet. You can't outrun a mutt, but the law? It's a cinch.

Go to #1.

#23 All the swell-looking dames are really giving you the once-over lately—curvy blondes, dark-eyed brunettes, playful redheads. Maybe it's because you changed your shirt this month.

Add 10 Magnetism points.
Go to (☆) location paragraph of your choice. See map.

#24 Brick-Nose cracks you across the base of the neck with his gun and runs after Carl. You drop fast but don't black out. His rush made it a feather-blow. You cut around a bend and hear a Luger's echoed pulse ring down the men's john. Brick-Nose flashes by a doorway. You pull your heater, crack two shots off, and hit him in the side of his skull. He flies back and down, twists over, and dies.

Go to #37.

#25   *Subtract D—1 Magnetism points.*

Half this scrublady's teeth are black and the other half are history. She uses ammonia like your least favorite aunt used cheap perfume. She swam in it. You hand her a line about being the landlord's younger brother, casing the joint, thinking about buying him out and all that comes with it, including her. She smiles and flaps an eyelid. You take a shot that it was supposed to be a wink. She leaves in a swoon. You drop back to Narcissa's door for an earful.

Go to #113.

#26   *Subtract D Magnetism points.*
Your man Carl is not listed.
Cross out a star at the Airport and try again.
Go to #1.

#27   *Subtract D+2 Moxie points.*

You spill to the girls how you bumped off all these guys, but how Charlie Cantrell says you're only gonna get a wrist-slap from the judge. You shot in self-defense, natch. The girls take your word for it and point their shaky, well-polished fingers toward Cantrell's office door.

Go to #14.

#28   Dino's is the kind of snazzy place that throws away good wine on creamy fish sauces and chicken gravy supremes, where you can't really taste the booze, let alone get pie-eyed on it. Inside a maitrè d' with some lip fuzz he probably calls a mustache twitches around like a puppet on strings, all wired up, yelling at everybody.

You try to muscle a table from him.
Go to #53.
or
Outside, you circle the dump and look for a service entrance.
Go to #101.

#29   The cute waitress you've been seeing spots you on the street, and she's real sore you haven't called. You say you're on a case, but she gets on yours. You sweet-talk her with promises of Paradise and two tickets to the fights.
Subtract 3 Magnetism points.
Go to (☆) location paragraph of your choice. See map.

#30   A swell looker at the ticket counter bats her big ones at you. You want a peek at the airline passenger list.
Go to #26.

#31   The scrublady takes her sweet time slapping her mop down the hall. You peek down the fire escape and across the street. Brick-Nose is still eating those tummy-tamers. Still the capped shadow you can't really make out, though you're not so sure anymore it's a copper. You lower your peepers to see through the hall window again, and catch the last swish from the old lady's fat rump as it turns the corner and she clumps downstairs.
     You climb back inside and get an earful through Narcissa's door.
Go to #113.

#32   Norris replaces his gat with his big mouth and pumps you with a blast of verbal slugs like he resents your job, he resents your kind of talk, he resents your age—you get the idea he doesn't like you a whole lot.

He says, "I protect Norma Vanderlip's interest, not some gumshoe. I advised her against your kind. We don't need you."

You say, "What are you, stuck on the old broad?" He goes to slug you but a hard look stops him cold.

"She was quite beautiful as a young lady," he says. "And still is."

"Too bad," you say. "Too bad you were just a lower-class guy . . . and still are." You leave. You'll see Mrs. V. some other time.

Cross out a star at the Vanderlip Estate.
Go to #1.

#33   You make Brick-Nose topple like a ten-story building on your chest. You should have popped him in his big, bad belly, since he was eating those medicine tablets like they were popcorn. He sticks his knee on your throat and slugs you across the side of your head with the Luger. Lights out.

Subtract D + 2 Muscle points.
Go to #102.

#34   Some musclebound Johnny steps out from the back with a chest what looks inflated with concrete. He wears a grimace like somebody stuck lime in his boxers. "This chump trouble?" he asks.

Judy backhands his forearm with a passing slap. "Ease up, Dan. He's a buddy."

"He want Narci?" he says. You figure this guy's got the Tarzan part down cold should Johnny Weissmuller kick. Or even Cheetah.

"Know any of Narcissa's boyfriends, Dan . . .?"

"Volner. Dan Volner," he spits. "What's it to you?"

You press him for a little more dope.
Go to #71.
or
You back off.
Go to #21.

#35   Norris gets off a lucky shot that ricochets off some rusty armor and into your side. You bleed all over the satin loveseat. Mrs. V. is gonna be sore as hell, you think before you die.
(You can start the case over on page 109.)

#36   You become part of a big black shadow, and the cops pass you by. Just a short pardon. There's too many streetcorners in this town with bright, accusing bulbs.
Go to #1.

#37   Carl shakes and bleeds against a tiled wall. He babbles about how he's been no good to nobody, how he didn't think he even hit that bum Sheen. "I shot," he mumbles. "I couldn't wait for the dough. Tired of waiting for things. We'd never get it. So I went, I shot, but didn't think I hit him. Then I ran scared. Just got bad genes—my mother says. Tough guys follow you. Bad genes follow you, too. Can't shake *them*, though. Part of your insides. Just can't sh—"

Carl's head turns, and his breathing ends. You search him and find a railroad ticket for a sleeper car and his .22-caliber pistol.

> *Cross out* a star at the Railroad Station.
> *Put a star* (☆) next to:
>   –The Vanderlip Estate
>   –City Hall.
> Go to #1.

#38   You dig up records that show that a Norma Lancer married Dawson Sheen, then got a divorce two years later. She took custody of their only child. Three years later, Norma Sheen married Dansforth Vanderlip II.

> *Cross out* a star next to City Hall.
> Go to #1.

#39   Roll the dice:
>   2–4, 10 go to #68.
>   5–9, 11, 12 go to #36.

#40   "Hey, Hart!" you yell.

Captain Hart jerks his head and tabs you being cuffed. He raises his hand and the blue boys stop squeezing you. So he remembers the time you fingered some toughs and gave *him* the headlines and the handshakes. He gets you off the hook with Riker. You tip your hat on the way out. Riker points his finger at you like it was a .38 ready to spring. "Next time," he says.

> Go to #1.

#41   Your car says "Goodnight, Irene" smack in the middle of evening traffic. You had a hunch this would happen when it started getting the heebie-jeebies three miles back.

> *Subtract 3 points from the M—M—M column of your choice.*
> Go to (☆) location paragraph of your choice. See map.

#42   Guy's got a skull like the Rock of Gibraltar. You pop a couple of knuckles with the blow. You just remembered his bad belly and his tablets. A punch there would have sent this hunk of meat to the pavement. But it's too late. He saps you with the Luger. Lights out.

> *Subtract D + 2 Muscle points.*
> Go to #102.

#43   You dream, all right. But like always, it winds up a nightmare. You catch a shadow on your smoky glass door. You can spot Lt. Riker's outline from a block off in a lousy fog at midnight. He bangs his fist on the door and asks you to open up as polite as he can. That means using no more than two four-letter words.

> Roll the dice:
>   2–8 go to #15.
>   9–12 go to #80.

#44   *Subtract D Muscle points.*
You shift your weight suddenly and your left shoulder drops. Meanwhile, your right hand shoots out like a blur full of knuckles. Norris sees half of you going east and half of you going west. He looks stunned, like his compass got jammed. He flinches and fires the .38 due north. That's where your noodle sits. Swell.

> Go to #126.

#45   This case is chewing up your insides. You need a stiff drink and a long sleep. Right now Sally Rand could knock you over with a feather or a blown kiss.
Subtract 3 Moxie points.
Go to (☆) location paragraph of your choice. See map.

#46   *Subtract D–2 Moxie points.*
Some broad in curlers lets out a shriek from her bed. Her old man looks beat and tells her to can the racket, and you buzz out of there.
Go to #110.

#47   *Subtract D–1 Muscle points.*
Go to #16.

#48   You happen across Moose Mason on the street. You start to smile until you remember you sent this mug up the river five years ago for assault. He remembers too, and you and his blackjack get reacquainted.
Subtract 3 Muscle points.
Go to (☆) location paragraph of your choice. See map.

#49   You pull the Persian rug out from under the desk and flip Norris head over heels. His skull thunks on the wood floor. You grab his gun and call the law.
Cross out a star at the Vanderlip Estate.
Go to #1.

#50   You figure you'll avoid the dizzy redhead at the desk somehow. You collar a bellhop for some dope.

Your boy Carl checked out. A bellhop says he looked like he was blowing town in a hurry.

Cross out a star at the Hotel Walton.
Go to #55.

#51   You hit cement and don't bounce.

Roll the dice:
      2–5 go to #18.
      6–12 go to #65.

#52   Cantrell's office is guarded by a harem of gal Fridays.

You jerk your shoulders back, fix your hat, and ask to see their sheik.
Go to #17.
or
You make like one of Cantrell's clients, a tough egg up for Murder One, and say you need to see him—bad.
Go to #27.

#53   *Subtract D–2 Muscle points.*
You say you want a table for one and pronto. "One what?" he says, twitching his lip fuzz.

You reach out and latch your fingers onto this monkey's suspender clips. The suspenders snap up like two big rubber bands and his pants fall down like a lead balloon. He snatches his trousers before they hit his knees and points to a table in the corner. You doff your hat and tell him to use a belt like other Joes.
Go to #60.

#54   You feel real good and real strong, like you could take on Jack Dempsey, your ex-wife, and Hitler—with both sets of knuckles tied behind your back.

Add 10 Muscle points.

Go to (☆) location paragraph of your choice. See map.

#55   *Put a star (☆) next to:*
—the Airport
—the Railroad Station
—the Docks.

(*But* there is only *one* correct choice out of the three, based on the clues revealed in this case; the other ones lead nowhere and cost M–M–M points. Choose wisely. Once you get to the correct location, you should not go on to either of the other two.)

Go to #1.

#56   Your right hand hits home and his bullet pulls wide of your skull and into Mrs. V.'s swank book-case. You picture her picking out what to read before beddy-bye and finding a lead slug poked her *Little Women*. Kind of embarrassing. Norris looks all proud and stupid, feeling for his jaw there on the fluffy rug. You pick up his rod.

Go to #32.

#57   He takes a swipe at your nose, but you deck him good with a pop to the temple. The redhead screams and tosses her fists at you. You head upstairs quick to find Carl.

>   *Subtract D–1 Muscle points.*
>   *Go to #11.*

#58   A big fat blonde in feathers and pumps swoops down on you and calls you a heel, flashing her blood-red fingernails like steak knives. Seems you finked on her loverboy awhile ago on some forgery scam. You give her the glad-eye, take her by the claw, and swear you'll make it up to her.

>   *Subtract 3 Magnetism points.*
>   *Go to (☆) location paragraph of your choice. See map.*

#59   People are partying and throwing confetti off a big boat that'll probably sink if it hits some driftwood. The good-timers on board wouldn't know the difference anyhow. And there's no sign of your man Carl on any passenger list.

>   *Subtract D–2 Moxie points or D–3 Muscle points.*
>   *Cross out a star at the docks and try again.*
>   *Go to #1.*

#60   Narcissa is parked at a candlelit table in a corner with some old guy, late fifties, in a dark green suit, and he's stroking her hand. You think, this bombshell sure gets around. But this mug's got a gray mustache and dyed hair as black as Jolson singing "Mammy."

He says something about, "I need it quick, sweet-heart," which makes her jerk her pretty mitt away. She says, "We're working on it." Some more words fly, words they can't put in Webster's. Narcissa gets up mad and leaves the place. Out of nowhere Brick-Nose appears, follows her outside, and strong-arms her.

"The boss don't like being left flat," he says, and starts slapping her silly. "Besides," he adds, "Nick was my buddy."

He's about to lay her out when you jump him from behind. But Brick-Nose shakes off your blow to his head with a shrug and bounces you a few times on the sidewalk like a yo-yo. Narcissa shows her gratitude by taking a quick powder. Brick-Nose gets tired of playing and takes off in a small truck with *Truman Warehouse* painted on the side. You sit and hold your head so it doesn't roll off your neck.

> *Subtract D + 2 Muscle points.*
> *Cross out a star at Dino's.*
> *Put a star (☆) next to your private eye office.*
> *Go to #1.*

#61   *Subtract D–2 Moxie points.*
Go to #16.

#62   You must think you're a regular kangaroo. Twenty feet from a dead standing position on a ledge, with an emphasis on the "dead" part.

You jump like Superman. Your arms are way out. Your fingers tingle, wanting to feel the cool stone of the opposite edge. And you gotta be a good ten feet short. You drop like a rock.

> *Roll the dice:*
>   *2–7 go to #51.*
>   *8–12 go to #107.*

#63   You ease into the study and case the room. Then you see if you can't dig up the rich dame, Mrs. V.
> *Go to #89.*

#64   You feel like hell. You have a three-day stubble on your face, a tongue as thick as a baloney, and bags under your eyes a bellhop wouldn't carry for less than a sawbuck.

Subtract 3 Moxie points.
Go to (☆) location paragraph of your choice. See map.

#65   You figure you broke your arm and cracked two ribs easy. You're as weak as a puppy and about as dumb.

Eliminate all Muscle points.
Go to #85.

#66   Narcissa's Boutique looks like some Greek went screwy with pillars and naked statues. Might be a great joint if you wanted to dress like the White Rock dame. Inside, you get your eyeful of a real goddess—a dark-skinned babe behind the counter with curves that'd give a sculptor the fits. She tags herself Judy Bostwick and she's been shop-girl there for the past year. Best of all, she likes you.

Go to #115.

#67   Louie "Creeps" Malone, an ex-con and known fence, runs up to your car and says he needs a lift to the harbor. You tell him to buzz off. He sticks a .38 in your ear so you can hear better. You tell him to hop in and make himself cozy.

Subtract 3 points from the M–M–M column of your choice,
worrying about the time slipping from your mitts.
Go to (☆) location paragraph of your choice. See map.

#68   The prowl car stops about an inch and a quarter from your big toe, and Officer Dooley hops out grinning.

"You been at the Mermaid when they were serving bullets instead of booze," he says. You play dumb, which comes easy for you, and he throws you in the car. You get taken downtown.
Go to #94.

#69   *Subtract D–5 Moxie points.*
You circle the building like some dumb Indian attacking a fort in a Ward Bond western. You maybe should beat it back to the reservation, redskin. The joint is boarded up but good. You spot movement up on the roof.

You see if there's a way inside from up there.
Go to #95.
or
You get in line for the frisk.
Go to #76.

#70   You feel like a regular wiseguy lately, cracking off to anyone in earshot. You're backchatting to cabbies, hotel clerks; you're even calling your landlady "sister."
Add 10 points to the M–M–M column of your choice.
Go to (☆) location paragraph of your choice. See map.

#71   "Just business," you say.
"Sounds like it's none of yours, mister."
Volner slams a hard, open palm flat on your soiled Arrow shirt. He grips cloth, buttons, and assorted chest hairs in his oversized meat-hook. He yanks you nose to nose. You feel like you're looking

up a nostril at Mount Rushmore. You've had enough of this swell time. You poke your .38 under his rib-cage and say, "Unless your maiden name is Clark Kent, chum, I bet I can pump lead faster than you can pump iron. What say?"

Subtract D Moxie points.

He starts to sweat like a moose. He says he's never seen a Cantrell, but he knows the Carl guy. "Smokes funny cigarettes," he says.

"How funny?" you say.

"They're all black," he says.

"That's real funny," you say. You put your rod away. Volner stands there like a kid who got spanked.

"Nice gun," Judy says. You like this dame.

Go to #116.

#72   You find some handwritten letters on notebook paper. One reads, "I know who you are. Remember that! The slum girl who makes good and finally marries into some big dough. Well, some of that dough should be spread around and real quick or else—"

Suddenly the study door opens and you slam the drawer shut. Norris steps in and pulls a shiny black .38 on you. You tell him to put the peashooter away. Maybe he listens, maybe he doesn't.

You try Moxie.
Go to #120.
or
You try Muscle.
Go to #44.

#73   Bad move. No chance you can outrun this mongrel all the way back to the Buick. You're as good as dog meat. The bowser leaps on your back and knocks you flat.
Subtract D–1 Muscle points.
When he's about to have one of your cheekbones for a snack a whistle stops him cold. It's the Mex. He ambles down to the hole you're trying to crawl into.
Go to #125.

#74   Your car says "Sayonara, Charlie" smack in the middle of noon traffic. You had a hunch this would happen when the piston heads started playing taps under the hood three miles back.
Subtract 3 points from the M–M–M column of your choice.
Go to (☆) location paragraph of your choice. See map.

#75   *Subtract D–3 Muscle points.*
Go to #72.

#76   When it's your turn to get frisked, you tell the baboon that if he squeezes too long or too hard, you're gonna stick your shoe up his nose.
Subtract D+2 Muscle points or D+2 Moxie points.
Go to #6.

#77   It hits you that when you latched your big ears onto Carl's phone-chatter at his place, he said he was "taking a sleeper." You thought maybe he was talking about the pill he popped, but you got wise and you realize he meant his one-way ticket out of this mess—by *train*. When you get to the station it's jammed with 9-to-5 suckers on the move home. They swing their attaché cases like ball-and-chains and scramble for the nearest bar car. You glimpse some

secretarial gam, then flinch in pain like you backed into an open lead pipe that caught you sharp in the ribs. Your lucky day—it's only the open muzzle to Brick-Nose's Luger poked halfway into your kidneys. "You seen him, shamus?" he asks.

"You look troubled," you say.

"You could say that, shamus," he says. "First it's my buddy, now the boss. Things need fixing. Just on my night off who'd a figured he'd get bumped? So now I got some evening-up to do, savvy?"

Suddenly, Carl turns a corner up ahead, stops short, and starts running hard down a far corridor. Brick-Nose looks away and shouts at Carl. You figure it's now or never. You jerk an elbow into Brick-Nose's belly, hoping it's still on the fritz.

Subtract D–2 Muscle points.

NOW—if you still have *plus* (+) Muscle points: Go to #109.

if you have *minus* Muscle points:
Roll the dice:
2–4 go to #2.
5–12 go to #109.

#78   You think it was some woman trucker from Paris once said, a warehouse is a warehouse is a warehouse. Only she didn't take a gander at this one with shiny cars out front and shiny-suited guys and their frails slipping in the back. You smell casino.

Inside, some baboon is frisking for rods. He takes his sweet time on the dames, too. You leave your .38 in the car.

You get in line for the frisk.
Go to #76.
or
You look for some other way to bust in.
Go to #69.

#79   Two coppers on patrol are tailing you so close they might as well sit in your trunk. You try to shake them.

Roll the dice:

    2–3   You bust onto one of those ugly new freeways and get the law dizzy in a concrete pretzel they call a cloverleaf. *Add 5 points to the M–M–M column of your choice.* Go to (☆) location paragraph of your choice. See map.

    4–6   You dodge into Fast Sammy's used car joint. The cops can't spot your junkheap in with all the other junkheaps. Go to (☆) location paragraph of your choice. See map.

  7–10   Can't shake them. *Subtract 2 points from the M–M–M column of your choice.* (Throw dice again.)

11–12 Can't shake them. *Subtract 5 points from the M–M–M column of your choice.* (Throw dice again.)

#80   You climb out the window and hit the fire escape. You hear Riker smash your door in. You slip into your neighbor's office. Sid the Dentist has got some dame with her choppers wide open like a scarlet hole and he's drilling for oil.

Sid doesn't even look up. "Riker again?" he says, playing with a molar.

"No," you say. "Greta Garbo."

"You're kidding?" he says, looking up. That's what you like about Sid. He's the only fella what takes you seriously. You run out of his office and clear of Riker.

Go to #1.

#81   The Mex sees you running toward him at full steam with the big bowser right behind. You figure the dog must be chums with the Mex and vice-versa, sharing the same yard and everything. You figure right. The Mex whistles and the bruiser stops cold. You catch your breath and stare at the dog. You'd bet your last dime he's laughing his mutt's butt off at you.

Go to #125.

#82   You look real spiffy. Your pants have only a few less wrinkles than those leatherskin cronies who read dime novels at the beach, and your trenchcoat looks like you slept in it for a month. It's only been a week and a half.

Subtract 3 Magnetism points.
Go to (☆) location paragraph of your choice. See map.

#83   *Subtract D Moxie points.*
Go to #92.

#84   While she's down on all fours cleaning up your mess, you glance at the register. Only "Carl" listed is in Room 14. You'll give it a looksee.
Go to #11.

#85   *Cross out* a star at Narcissa's apartment.
Go to #1.

#86   He grins. You grin. He saps you on the skull with his Luger for effect. You should have kicked him in that bad belly of his, since he was eating those medicine tablets like popcorn. At least that's what you're thinking when you go down for the count.
Subtract D+4 Muscle points.
Go to #102.

#87   Some mug is tailing you. He's your average-looking hard guy, not quite as tall as the Chrysler building. You feel frisky and confront him. He bounces a blackjack off your head.
Subtract 3 Muscle points.
Go to (☆) location paragraph of your choice. See map.

#88   Your office offers the comforts of an old sock. The smells too, so you open a window. Outside, the city lays there in a haze of heavy sunlight. You look up Truman Warehouse in the phone book, but the minute you put your feet up to think, the phone rings. It's Mrs. Vanderlip. She sounds upset, like one of her dinner guests got gas during dessert. You tell her you'll be there pronto, and hang up. You stick your feet back up, watch the haze, and for a time, you dream.
Cross out a star at your private eye office.

Put a star (☆) next to:
  —the Vanderlip Estate
  —Truman Warehouse.
Go to #43.

#89   You surprise the Mrs. resting in the drawing room. She doesn't see you straight off, and with her gray hair scrambled and her face blank and lost, she almost looks kind of soft. Almost. She shoots a look at you with the force of a magnum.

"What do you think you are doing?" she barks, doing a swell impersonation of her bowser.

"Trying to get a line on an old moneyed dame and her being cagey," you say. ". . . And motherhood." Her eyes grow harder. "I knew this 'dear daughter' routine didn't cut much ice from the word go," you say, "but after what happened at the railroad station—"

"What are you—you jabbering about?" she stammers. "Get out!"

"This blue-letter blackmail means beans," you say, "compared to the other shakedown you never came clean about—those notes from a certain party better forgotten who never let you forget."

She reels, "How did you—Norris! Norris!"

"Ain't you supposed to *ring* for help?" you ask. "You never learned this high-society bit too good, did you?"

The more you talk like a street Johnny, the more she steams. Norris pops out from behind the door, there all along. He holds his rag in one hand and his .38 in the other. You're fed up to the ears with gun barrels pointing at you all day.

Norris says, "Never mention that pig in Mrs. Vanderlip's presence—ever!"

"Norris," she says, "where did you get that gun? I don't understand."

"You're worse than an old bat," you tell her, "'cause you're twice as blind." Norris flinches, fires. You dive behind a desk. The old broad faints.

NOW—if you still have *plus* (+) Moxie points: Go to #49.

if you still have *minus* (–) Moxie points:
Roll the dice:
2–4 go to #35.
5–12 go to #49.

#90   Norris follows you into Mrs. V.'s living room and looks real sore at you, natch. At least he looks at you. Mrs. V. thinks you get leprosy if you look at puffy-faced dicks. She's in a feather robe and strikes a pose from the last act of *Camille*. You wish you had a rotten tomato. She cries how the worst has come, how you've botched it all, how you were too late. She jams a letter on blue stationery under your snoot. It's a nifty blackmail note. It says: "Your daughter, Narcissa, keeps poor company. People in your position wouldn't want business and social contacts to be aware of such 'associations.' You need protection. . . ."

It jabbers on and finally lays out a lump-sum payoff of $200,000. Chicken feed for this fat hen, but she's still squawking. "You have to find this despicable character," she says. "The slime Narcissa calls her beau is obviously trying to ruin the Vanderlip name."

"Ever been blackmailed before?" you ask.

Her cheeks show red. "Never," she says. "What do you take me for?"

"A lying floozy," you say. "But it's your dough." Norris goes to pull his gat, but you sock him square

on the nose and snap his neck back so hard his cap flips across the room. He reels and falls flat on his back.

Subtract D–2 Muscle points.

"Better keep the palace guard in line, queenie," you tell her. "Bad manners pulling rods on guests in the drawing room." You walk out past Norris, who's holding his bloody nose.

Objectives #6 and #7: Who is blackmailing Mrs. Vanderlip? Why?

Cross out a star at the Vanderlip Estate.
Put a star (☆) next to:
    —Narcissa's apartment
    —the Hotel Walton.
Go to #1.

#91   Your car says "Adios, Muchachos" smack in the middle of morning traffic. You had a hunch this would happen when the engine started doing the rumba three miles back.

Subtract 3 points from the M–M–M column of your choice.
Go to (☆) location paragraph of your choice. See map.

#92   You case the place and hit upon Sheen's library. Tucked inside a notebook, you find some IOUs. Heavy IOUs. The kind that could break your back just by the weight of the zeros in the numbers. There are a half-dozen or so of these gambling debts, and they're all signed "C.V." Whoever "C.V." is, he obviously owes a stack of green stuff to the casino.

You spot a light flick on in the house next door and the dark-haired face of some middle-aged dame presses up against a window. It flattens out her features like she was socked hard with a frying pan in a Bugs Bunny cartoon. You dodge from sight.

Then you notice the lamp above the back porch has been on. It splashes a yellow light on the endless rock garden and on a dull red blanket. Ten feet closer, you see that the rock garden isn't endless—it quits at the driveway—and that the dull red blanket isn't a blanket—it's a dead man in a bathrobe. In fact, it's the old guy with the dyed hair from Dino's. The "D.S." on his robe tells you it ain't Dinah Shore. A .38-caliber hole split his initials to his heart. The slob, probably woken up by something, checked it out and found a bullet. You check out the driveway and the dirt near-by. A couple of sets of footprints there—one set close, a different set further back. Probably Brick-Nose coming a little too late to save the boss from the Mob. Sleeping on the job. Bad for a hood's rep. Sleeping. Brings back memories. You try to remember whether you close your eyes when you do that.

Objectives #4 and #5: Who killed Dawson Sheen? Why?

Cross out a star at Sheen's house.
Go to #108.

#93   Your right hand connects with his jaw. The bullet swerves and cuts a path of blood across your cheek.

Subtract D–2 Muscle points.

You grab the gun as the old guy hits the floor. "Now you got me staining Mrs. V.'s rug she probably got from some strange, far-off burg like China or Oakland," you say.

Norris looks all proud and stupid, feeling for his jaw there on the fluffy rug. You pick up his rod.

Go to #3?

#94   In the interrogation room they grill you good. They keep calling you "pally" and siccing some lug with long nasal hairs on you. Give these badges credit. They play rough and know where it hurts.

Subtract one die roll from your weakest M–M–M column.

They've got nothing to hold you on except maybe three counts of exposing facial stubble on public property. They toss you out on the seat of your trench.

Go to #1.

#95   You climb off a side ladder to the roof. As your head pops up from below the edge of the wall, so does the barrel of a .32, and it's poking you in the forehead. Attached to the trigger is the finger from some Johnny playing casino guard.

"You want in or you come up for the view?" he says.

"Not much to see," you say, "except a piece of lead stuck in the far end of that rod you're pointing."

"Yeah, it ain't much of a tourist spot," he says, sticking the gun in your eyeball. "Maybe it's the building downstairs you want. Only you go in like everybody else and get frisked. Got me?"

You nod and backpedal down the ladder smiling. They usually don't plug you if you're smiling. Usually.

Subtract D–1 Moxie points.
Go to #76.

#96   You stop in at a local joint and buy a bottle of good hooch to give you that extra pep. Besides, you couldn't think of anything else for dinner.

Add 10 points to the M–M–M column of your choice.
Go to (☆) location paragraph of your choice. See map.

#97   Outside the apartment house, you see Brick-Nose impersonating a lamppost across the street. He's always dipping his mitt into his pocket and fishing out tablets he dumps into his mouth. You figure he must have a bad belly. On another corner, a capped shadow ducks out of sight. You figure it must be a cop. Maybe the law even got the same dope about Narcissa you did, and put a tail on her.

Three floors up, at Narcissa's number, you stick your ear against the door to try and hear some chitchat inside.

Go to #114.

#98   Sheen's house overlooks a thick stretch of palms and a rock garden that winds and disappears into darkness. There's no lights and no answer at the door. You slip across the lawn and look for an unlocked window.

You find one—the upper bathroom—and you squeeze through like a clumsy second-story man hauling too much fat.

Go to #83.

or

You don't find one, so you take your hat, cover your fist, and bust a few panes, hoping no alarm starts screaming.

Go to #103.

#99   You run into ex–Detective Sergeant Murphy, a crooked cop from way back, who's pounding a beat now instead of serving time like he oughtta. You crack wise about his feet getting flatter, so he saps you for the exercise.

Subtract 3 Muscle points.
Go to (☆) location paragraph of your choice. See map.

#100   Inside, you mouse around the flat and a picture on the bedroom dresser grabs your eye. It's the Vanderlip estate, front view, with four people standing straight as iron in the doorway. Mrs. V., a good fifteen years younger, has her mitts on the shoulders of a cute blond girl no more than six. A bald, pale, wiry man is left of Battle-ax. Probably Mr. V. Even alive, he looked dead. Then there's a boy. He's maybe fifteen, got his arms folded and a puss on his face that says, Thanks for nothing. It's a weak face, easily hated and hating.

You rustle through some drawers and find bankbooks, Judy Bostwick's résumé with her phone number circled, and piles of blue stationery. Feet shuffle outside the apartment door. You hustle out onto the fire escape and hear Narcissa talking to someone, some guy. You can't make out his voice, but he's hot.

"It was panic," she says. "Must have panicked."

"What? Like the last time?" he growls. "Was that panic, too?"

"That was protection. Someone had to protect me," she says accusingly. "That lug had his hands all over—"

He interrupts, "No excuse, baby, no damn excuse."

Narcissa swings into the bedroom. You press up to the brick wall like it was Rita Hayworth just so she doesn't spot you. He follows her, saying, "What about our marriage plans? This 'responsibility' of yours is destroying—" She slams the window down, pulls the shade. Swell. You hop off the fire escape and crawl along the ledge.

You look down three stories and see a lot of cement and clotheslines. Across the way, about twenty feet or so, is another ledge. Next to you is another window to someone else's apartment. It's open, and you hear some sheets rustle. This human fly routine is getting plenty stale.

You try to jump to the other ledge.
Go to #62.
or
You crawl through the adjacent window.
Go to #46.

#101   *Subtract D Moxie points.*

Will Rogers once said he never met a guy he didn't like. You can't go that far. The closest you get is you never met a parking attendant you couldn't bribe. Case in point: Dino's parking kid — Harry. Harry takes a five-spot from you and gets you in through the kitchen entrance. You push past the pots and pans to the swinging doors to the dining room. You peek through the square glass window and just miss getting popped in the jaw with the door by a waiter with a tray of leftover grub.

Go to #60.

#102   *Cross out a star at the Hotel Walton.*
Go to #1.

#103   *Subtract D–3 Muscle points.*
Go to #92.

#104   A four-eyed twerp is sitting on his keester, reading a magazine and looking real smug. He squeaks about how no company information is disclosed to unauthorized personnel.

You yank him three feet up by the collar and tell him to speak the lingo, Jack.
Go to #47.
or
You tell him you're the boss's brother-in-law and you like to squeal on loafing twerps.
Go to #61.

#105   You figure the truth will get you out of this jam or it's curtains.

"I wanted to know if you were his best gal because I wanted to tell you easy. But with that cannon looking to split me down the middle from the inside out, I guess I gotta tell you straight."

She doesn't move.

"Sheen's dead," you say. "And I was off to call the law."

She doesn't move.

"I said, somebody killed Sheen. He's soaking up the moonlight in his lounge chair out back. Only he's soaking the chair with his blood, too."

"How do I know it wasn't you?" she says, shaking.

"Do I look like a killer?" you say.

She cocks the hammer on the shotgun. Sometimes your mouth flaps around without the benefit of your brain.

"Look," you say, "you see anybody come around here tonight?"

"I just got home a couple hours ago," she says, "Didn't see anybody but you, Mr. Snoop."

"So are we calling the cops or what?" you say.

"He's dead, huh?" She looks scared now.

"A hole in his chest says so," you say. "You don't believe me, go have a looksee."

She leads you back to poolside. When she sees Sheen all stiff-like, she goes limp for a second and you snatch the shotgun from her. She doesn't seem to care, and falls on her knees. She buries her head in Sheen's shoulder and cries up a real storm.

You unload the shotgun, drop it, then march back to you car. Let her mourn the bum in peace.

Go to #1.

#106   It isn't Hart. What it is is a long afternoon on the hot seat with Riker.

        Go to #94.

#107   Somebody up there must think you're swell, 'cause you land in an open garbage bin and only sprain your arm and bruise some ribs. You smell bad, though, with garbage all over you.

        Subtract D + 5 Muscle points.
        Go to #85.

#108   As you slide down the driveway as quiet as you know how, a dame's voice cracks the silence. You turn and look behind you. There's the next-door neighbor, her face normal now, if you call that snoot on her normal. It sticks out as far as the shotgun she's got tight in her mitts.

"What are you doing over there, mister?" Her eyes are squeezed together like she's ready to take a bead on you and let the pellets fly. She's too far away to muscle before the shotgun blast would bounce your skull up against the house across the street. You can maybe charm her.

"I was looking for Mr. Sheen," you say. "You his good-looking girlfriend he's always yapping about?"

Subtract D Magnetism points.

She laughs, half at herself, mostly at you. You're in a real jam, brother.

NOW—if you still have *plus* (+) Magnetism points: Go to #105.
if you have *minus* (–) Magnetism points:
      Roll the dice:
          2–9 go to #105.
          10–12 go to #20.

#109   You're one lucky Joe. Brick-Nose's tummy is still tender. He buckles, but he's quick and swipes at you with his mitt and spins you around.

    Go to #24.

#110   *Cross out a star* at Narcissa's apartment.

You hear a prowl-car siren wailing your way. Maybe somebody saw your high-wire act and called for the net.

    Roll the dice:
        2–9 go to #122.
        10–12 go to #22.

#111   You forgot the Mex said they usually put the pooch in the game room. You remember but quick since the mutt sinks his teeth in your good trousers

and even better ankle. You fall back out the window with the dog yowling and limp to the study window.
Subtract D–1 Muscle points.
Go to #63.

#112   Good target. This guy's got a nose like a brick, but his belly is Jell-O. You remembered his bad stomach and the tablets he was eating like they were popcorn. He folds in two at the blow and drops the Luger. You kick it away and yank his head up.

"I'll lay off who I want," you say. You leave him there with your footprint in his tummy.
Go to #102.

#113   You hear Narcissa say, "Don't do anything stupid, Carl. Please. Leave it to me. We'll get the money. It'll take time. Just be calm. Please, honey."

Footsteps head toward the door, so you use the nearest broom-closet for cover. The greasy Joe from the Mermaid Club comes out looking like he wrapped himself around a good bottle of hooch and found it hard to let go. He grabs Narcissa at the door and holds her. He says, "Remember—the Hotel Walton." She nods. Then he leaves. Back at the door, you hear Narcissa get on the phone and say, "Yes—I'll be there later for dinner, okay? Dino's. Yes, I know it."

You walk outside and nobody's in sight. No shadow. No Brick-Nose. Just an alley cat looking for trouble. Not like you. You never have to look. It's your business.
Cross out a star at Narcissa's apartment.
Put a star (☆) next to:
    —the Hotel Walton
    —Dino's.
Go to #124.

#114   *Subtract D Moxie points.*

You hear two voices from inside and a large clanging metal bucket from outside. Which means you don't hear jack, because the scrubwoman is making a racket coming up the stairs to your floor.

You duck onto the fire escape outside the hallway window and wait till the mop-haired broad passes.
Go to #31.
or
You use your magnetism to make her amscray quick so you don't miss any palaver at the apartment door.
Go to #25.

#115   *Subtract D + 2 Magnetism points.*

Judy fingers her jade necklace and tells you she thinks Narcissa is off her noodle. All her mom's dough and she won't take a dime. She hates her mom. So she runs this place to get by and get free. "Which, by the way, *I* am Tuesday night," she says. You make a note of these facts and ask who Narcissa plays around with.

"Some lawyer hotshot," she says, "Charlie Cantrell. Works at the Rollins Building. And another guy, Carl Reagan, who's real trouble, partly 'cause he's a lush, mostly 'cause he carries trouble with him. You can feel it. He works at Fanger Plastics."

You say you'll get in touch. She hopes you mean that literally.
Go to #34.

#116   *Cross out* a star at Narcissa's Boutique.
                Put a star (☆) *next to:*
                    –Cantrell's Office
                    –Fanger Plastics.
                Go to #1.

#117   You blow through red lights plenty fast, hoping the coppers are eyeing sidewalk nylons or taking siestas, two of the three things they're real good at. The other is breaking your chops whenever possible.

        Go to (☆) location paragraph of your choice. See map.

#118   Some dumb gunsel has been following you for blocks, probably holding a gat and a grudge. You try to shake him fast.

        Roll the dice:

                2–3   Can't shake him. *Subtract 5 points from the M–M–M column of your choice.* (Throw dice again.)

                4–7   Can't shake him. *Subtract 2 points from the M–M–M column of your choice.* (Throw dice again.)

                8–10 You duck into Wang Lee's laundry and hide behind the dirty towels. The gunsel loses you. You throw a few yen to Wang for the consideration. Go to (☆) location paragraph of your choice. See map.

                11–12 You turn on the gunsel in an alley and flatten his nose for him. *Add 5 points to the M–M–M column of your choice.* Go to (☆) location paragraph of your choice. See map.

#119   At the Vanderlip Estate:
                if *no* stars are crossed out, go to #128.
                if *one* star is crossed out, go to #8.
                if *two* stars are crossed out, go to #9.

#120   *Subtract D–1 Moxie points.*

"Look," you say, "I'm just trying to protect your boss-lady's interest. The more I know, the better I can do my job."

His face grows hard with deep-grooved wrinkles and his trigger finger twitches. He ain't buyin' your bill of goods. Another twitch and you're going to get ventilated. You've got to muscle him and plenty quick.

Go to #44.

#121   You give the once-over to the dumb, gum-popping redhead perched like a stuffed bird at the front desk. You could count this babe's I.Q. on the thumb of one hand. You distract her by knocking the inkwell clear across the desk and onto her new nylons. You say you're really sorry, a clumsy ape, but while she's crying and carrying on trying to blot her thighs, you try and sneak a look at the register to find Carl's room number.

Subtract D Moxie points. Go to #84.
or
Subtract D–1 Magnetism points. Go to #127.

#122   The cops cut you off at the far end of the alley and nab you on the run. They drag you down to the precinct house for rubbing up against skyscrapers without a license. They also figure Lt. Riker would like a friendly chat with you. You think you spot Capt. Hart, who could pull you out of this spot.

> **Roll the dice:**
>> **2–7 go to #40.**
>> **8–12 go to #106.**

#123   Seems you paid him. And he owes *you*. Three nags got themselves disqualified in the seventh after the race, so your filly pulled into the money finishing third. You feel swell.

> *Add 10 points to the M–M–M column of your choice.*

You ask if "Ponies" saw a nervous slick-haired guy smoking dark cigarettes. In other words, your boy Carl. "Ponies" says, "Sure. He was hailing a cabbie. Had two bags with him. I'd say he was blowing town in a hurry."

You thank "Ponies" with eight bits for a paper and the info, and race back to the Buick.

> **Cross out a star at the Hotel Walton.**
> **Go to #55.**

#124   Speaking of trouble, a black and white heap with the law inside cruises by and you hope they don't spot you. Not that you've done anything you wouldn't tell your mother, but you're always on Lt. Riker's Ten Most Wanted.

> **Go to #39.**

#125   The tattered Mex says, "Sorry, señor, he must have got out. Duke, he always stay in the game room." The Mex shows his gold teeth.

"Everything is jake," you say, but you walk back on the brick road knowing a Mex scarecrow saved your cowardly lion's hide.

Go to #90.

#126   Roll the dice:
         2–5, 11 go to #93.
         6–10, 12 go to #56.

#127   When she's on her knees wiping up your mess, you eyeball the register and see Room 14 has a "Carl" somebody in it. The redhead rises real close to your lapels. You can smell her ruby lipstick. You say you'll make it up to her. She chuckles.

"But I betcha can't make it up ta *him*," she says.

"Who him?" you say. You turn and see a good-looking gent in a black striped suit.

"You the manager?" you ask.

"That's right," he says. You smile.

"For a minute there I thought you were her husband," you say.

"That too," he says, holding his knuckles. You get the feeling you should have used some moxie here.

Go to #57.

#128   By the time you get from the gate to the house, you figure you must be in Jersey. The Vanderlip driveway makes Route 66 look like a cowpath.

You get ants in your pants while some over-starched servant goes to announce you, so you dodge into Mrs. V.'s study to sniff around. Your shnozz leads you to her private desk. You shouldn't pry, but what the hey.

> You jimmy her desk drawer open real easy.
> **Go to #130.**
> *or*
> You yank it out like a bad tooth.
> **Go to #75.**

#129   No answer. You use the hard celluloid that covers your driver's license and wedge it between the lock and doorjamb. Presto—it opens. You're a damn magician sometimes. You wish you could saw the older Vanderlip dame in half and lose the pieces.
> *Subtract D Moxie points.*
> **Go to #100.**

#130   *Subtract D–1 Moxie points.*
> **Go to #72.**

Hard-Boiled Points (Case B) (220 points)

Objective #1: Charles Cantrell (business lawyer for Dawson Sheen) is Narcissa's boyfriend.   <u>10</u> points

Objectives #2 and #3: Carl Vanderlip (Reagan) *actually* killed Little Boy Blue . . .   <u>25</u> points

. . . because he and Brick-Nose were putting the squeeze on Reagan for the money he owed Sheen, and Reagan didn't have it; *and/or* Little Boy Blue was having fun hurting his sister, Narcissa.   <u>25</u> points

Objectives #4 and #5: Norris (Mrs. Vanderlip's chauffeur) *actually* killed Dawson Sheen . . .   <u>40</u> points

. . . because Sheen was blackmailing Mrs. Vanderlip and threatening to topple her social status by exposing their earlier marriage and gambling associations. (Obviously, Norris loved and protected Mrs. V.)   <u>35</u> points

Objectives #6 and #7: Dawson Sheen was blackmailing Mrs. Vanderlip . . .   <u>15</u> points

. . . because he needed the money to save the casino.   <u>20</u> points

—Narcissa (and Carl, but *not* Carl alone) was blackmailing her mother . . .   <u>25</u> points

. . . because she wanted to help her brother get the money to pay off his debts at the casino. (Their mother had disowned him and the past husband/father he was part of.)   <u>25</u> points

Hard-Boiled Rating (Case C)

170–220 points	One Tough Egg
120–165 points	Gumshoe with Guts
45–115 points	Soft-Boiled Shamus
0–40 points	Near-Sighted Peeper

★ ★ ★ ★ ★ ★ ★

The Final Dope (Case C)

You're doing a quick looksee at the daily sheet for some box scores when whose mug should be stuck on a page four crime wrap-up but Mrs. V.'s. She's busting her way through the press boys outside the State courthouse, and by the looks of the body-count in the background, she decked an army of them before this flash caught her. She's in a rotten mood. She just had her chauffeur sent up the river and her social status down the toilet. For all the steam she's giving off and the indignity on her face, the caption should still read "My life is a bunch of malarky."

You're feeding yourself another helping of hooch when in pops the happy couple, Mr. and Mrs. Charles Cantrell. Narcissa looks windblown and free, like someone yanked the anchor off of her neck. She floats up to you with a smile that's been tanned and nursed by the sun. Cantrell is as big a stiff as ever. He shakes your hand like he was Robby the Robot.

"We've come to give you what my mother owed you and more," Narcissa says. "It's the least we can do." She gives Cantrell a nudge that must have put a dent in his ribs.

"Yeah, sorry about the rough-stuff back in the office," he says. "No hard feelings, scout." He slaps three hundred smackers folding on your desk. You haven't seen that many presidents together since the last election.

"Thanks," you say. "Hope things work out better for you two."

Narcissa's eyes go dim. "Better than in the past, yes," she says. "We gave you some special kind of case, didn't we?"

You rub your stubble awhile and say, "Daughter hates mother. Mother hates son. Father hates mother. Mother shuns son. Daughter blackmails mother to help brother. Father blackmails mother to help himself. Son hates himself and thinks he kills father, if he ever really knows it *is* his father in the first place. . . . And the butler did it."

You slug down another jigger of Scotch. "Run-of-the-mill American family, in my book," you say. "Nothing special."

"Norris wasn't a butler," Cantrell says. "He was a chauffeur."

You hate guys what ruin good stories with factual details.

"Yeah," you say, "some chauffeur. He didn't haul her around with any limo I know of. He used a pedestal. Here's some low-class lug trying all his life to protect a snooty dame's honor she never had in the first place. I should have known it was him earlier, seeing the Vanderlip meat-wagon all the time and thinking some uniformed shadow was the law. It was Norris all along, staking out your brother. His were the second set of footprints I found behind Carl's in Sheen's backyard. Norris was going to make sure Carl didn't hurt Mrs. V.'s rep any, that's for sure. And when he saw the opportunity to get rid of Sheen *and* put the finger on Carl? The old guy plugged Sheen after Carl had just run off in his usual panic, not knowing if his own shots hit the mark or not. You two honeymoon any yet?"

"No," Narcissa says. "We're just on our way. Charles is closing his office for two weeks and I'm letting Judy take over my shop while I'm gone."

Your ears prick up like Lassie hearing it's chowtime. "Judy?" you say. "You mean that sexy dish with the eyes no lug could forget unless he's a dumb shamus who forgets if he's wearing shoes or not?"

"Judy Bostwick," says Narcissa. "That's her." You pick up the phone. "You want her number?" she chuckles.

"No thanks, honey," you say. "I just remembered I saw it laying on top of some blue stationery somewhere."

Narcissa starts laughing and you start dialing.

Cantrell just stands there like someone asked him to be spontaneous.

THE END
(Case C)
"MONEY NEVER BLEEDS"